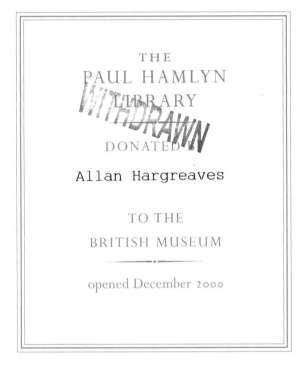

HISTORY OF
MYTHS RETOLD

First published in Great Britain in 1998
by Hamlyn. This edition published in 2000 by
Chancellor Press, an imprint of Bounty Books,
a division of the Octopus Publishing Group Ltd,
2–4 Heron Quays, London, E14 4JP

ISBN 0 75370 292 4

Produced by Toppan (HK) Ltd

Printed in China

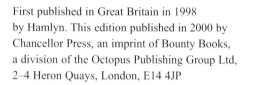

HISTORY OF
MYTHS RETOLD

Diana Ferguson

CHANCELLOR
PRESS

Introduction   6

CREATION & DESTRUCTION   16
   Dividing the Waters   18
   Fire and Ice   20
   Fishing up the World   24
   Izanagi and Izanami   26
   The Parting of Heaven and Earth   28
   Old Spider and the Clam Shell   30
   The Turtle's Shell   32
   Michabo and the Flood   34
   Churning the Ocean of Milk   36
   The Death of Balder the Beautiful   38
   Ragnarok   44

ELEMENTS & CELESTIAL BODIES   46
   The Sun in Hiding   48
   The Disappearing Moon   50
   How Night turned into Day   52
   The Evening Star   54

The Mist and the Rainbow   56
Sky Spirit and Fine Weather
   Woman   60
The Cowherd and the Heavenly
   Spinner   62
Ulysses and the Bag of Winds   64
Coyote and the Theft of Fire   66
Prometheus and the Theft of Fire   68

LIFE & DEATH   70
   The Golden Apples of Idun   72
   Gilgamesh   76
   The Message of Unkulunkulu   84
   Maui and the Waters of Life   86
   Lightning and the Sack of Storms   88

MAGIC & MYSTERIES   90
   Odin and the Mead of All-Knowing   92
   Orpheus and the Music of
   Enchantment   96

The God on the Gallows	100
Taliesin of the Shining Brow	102
The Spider that Spins	106
The Secret of Weaving	108

VEGETATION & FERTILITY 110
Ishtar and Tammuz	112
Isis and Osiris	116
How Winter Came into the World	120
Mondamin and the Indian Corn	124
Dionysos and the Vine	128
Echo and Narcissus	130

JOURNEYS & CONQUESTS 132
Durgâ and the Demon	134
Master of Many Arts	136
Perseus and the Gorgon	138
The Coming of Hercules	142
The Labours of Hercules	144
The Bulls from the Sea	152

Indra, Vishnu and the Demon of Drought	158

LOVE & MARRIAGE 160
Cupid and Psyche	162
Artemis and Acteon	168
The Sorrows of Branwen	170
Lleu Llaw Gyffes and the Flower-Faced Maiden	176
Little Star and the Chief's Daughter	180

Glossary of Names	182
Bibliography	184
Index	186
Acknowledgements	192

INTRODUCTION

Step inside the pages of this book and you will find, like pressed flowers in some forgotten volume, a whole cast of characters waiting to break free. Out they tumble, this unruly horde of gods, goddesses, demons, nymphs, giants, dwarves, spirits and supernaturals, and all up to their usual tricks – brewing up concoctions in cauldrons, flying through the air in feather cloaks, eating magic fruit, sitting with their feet in virgins' laps, stirring up cosmic seas, driving cattle across the sky where cattle have no business to be, dying horrible deaths and bouncing back to life again, turning people to stone at the flick of an eyelid, prattling on even after their heads have been severed from their bodies, turning feathers into snowflakes without so much as an 'excuse-me', and endlessly

metamorphosing – into bulls, cows, snakes, birds, vines, sheaves of corn, stars, clouds, winds, lightning, showers of gold, columns of sea foam, and any other such phantasmagorical nonsense as happens to suit their present fancy – and all the while jostling each with the other, to be the one most remembered by posterity for this or that particular feat.

A LADDER TO THE MOON

Such are the characters that inhabit myth, and they have been behaving in this way for thousands of years. The stage on which these characters enact their tales is not all open to the eye at once: there are deeper meanings waiting their turn in the wings, some of which are extremely profound and give myths the power to touch us at the deepest level, in ways to which we are unaccustomed in our frenetic, materially driven daily lives. And the outer form chosen by myth to impart these deeper meanings is, quite simply, story; for myths are, first and foremost, ripping good yarns, hearty dollops of soul-nourishing narrative.

If myths are stories, it is interesting to look at where they fit in the storyteller's repertoire, for there is more than one category of story. There are, of course, the ordinary, everyday anecdotes told about real people in the real world, the kind of retelling of an observed event or reminiscence that might be shared within a family or familiar group. Then there are folk tales, which still have a homely feeling but which are beginning to deal with larger issues. These are peopled by fictitious but still recognizably real characters, and sometimes introduce an element of fantasy in the form of anthropomorphic animals, such as spiders or hares, that can talk. The trickster, who is able to outwit others through his natural cunning, is a favourite figure in folk tale.

Take a step further into the land of the imagination and we move into the 'wide, wide world' of the wonder tale, inhabited by fictitious princes, princesses, witches, animal helpers and a whole cast of otherworldly characters. The main action of the wonder tale is a form of trial or initiation, which takes place in a realm 'out there', a barely glimpsed dimension beyond the bounds of the ordinary – the magic forest, the land beneath the sea, the meadows of the underworld – where anything can and does happen, and where appearances are never to be trusted.

Then there are legends, based around the adventures of historical or semi-historical figures. The fabric of these stories is woven from skeins of both fact and fantasy that are so closely intermingled that it is impossible to separate the two.

If folk and wonder tales are the popular tunes and traditional ballads of the story-teller's repertoire, myths are its grand opera. Here strut all the great gods and goddesses, wielding thunderbolts, riding through the sky, creating worlds, enjoying the pleasures of eternal youth, and indulging in such other pastimes as omnipotence and immortality allow. Myths address such grand, archetypal themes as the origins of the human race, and

BELOW: An ivory statuette of a chubby Vishnu, seated on the serpent Sesha and holding a shell, a mace, a disc and a lotus, which recall the treasured stone, spear, sword and cup of the Irish gods. One of the chief Hindu gods, Vishnu's sphere was the cosmic stage.

what fate lies in wait for us after we have died.

Another feature that distinguishes the different types of story is whether or not the characters are named. In folk and wonder tales they often remain nameless, as if they stand for Everyman or Everywoman. In myths and legends, the names of the chief protagonists are almost always given for they are

personalities in their own right, with their own particular attributes that often serve a useful function in moving the story along.

As the different types of stories play out their narratives before us, they change in scope, the domestic hearth turning into the universal stage of the cosmos. Irish storytellers have a wonderful analogy for the relationship between the various story forms: they call it 'a ladder to the moon'. As the British storyteller Ben Haggarty puts it, '... and so you've gone from the incidental – the stories of everyday life – to stories of the beginning of everything. And in Ireland, that's called a ladder to the moon. The first rung is here on earth with us and at the top is the moon and how it came to be. And you can't get to the top without stepping on every single rung.'

MYTH AND RELIGION

All myths come from what was once, or still is, a living belief system about the world in which we live, our relationship to it, and the great imponderables of the origins of existence, life after death, and the nature of divinity. When such a body of belief is still active, it is known as a religion, for example the modern world religions of Christianity, Islam and Buddhism. When it no longer has influence over the way a people see the world and lead their lives, it is shunted off into the siding of 'mythology', a term taken to mean a set of outworn beliefs invented by primitive and child-like minds, that provide amusement and interest but cannot be taken seriously – 'myths', in fact.

On closer examination, however, such distinctions become spurious. The same basic questions exercise our minds as did those of people living in, say, Sumeria or Egypt five thousand years ago, and it is profoundly moving to be able, through the medium of myth, to reach out across the centuries and, as it were, take the hand of our ancestors in a shared attempt to unravel the mysteries of life.

Different world views, call them religion, mythology, or what you will, arise at different points along the continuum of developing human consciousness. This continuum may be compared to an underground runner that

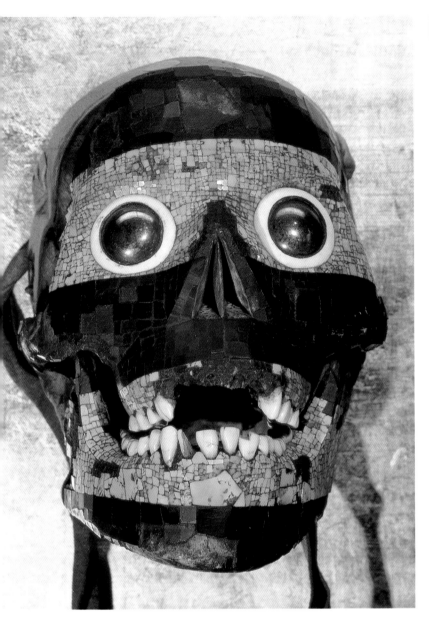

LEFT: THE MASK OF THE AZTEC GOD
TEZCATLIPOCA, MADE OF LIGNITE AND
TURQUOISE ARRANGED OVER A HUMAN SKULL.
AS A PAIR, THE DEVIOUS TEZCATLIPOCA AND
HIS BROTHER, THE PEACEFUL QUETZALCOATL,
EXPRESSED THE DUALITY OF GOOD AND EVIL.

as surely as your height and colouring have
been determined by the genes you inherited.
Indeed, some of the patterns and details of
Christ's life story are almost identical with
those of certain sacrificial saviour gods
worshipped in earlier pagan pantheons.

Such comparisons need not give rise to
conflict – indeed, far from it. While fundamen-
talists might argue that the symbolic events in
Christ's life story are totally unique and owe
nothing to any other source, when one realizes
that there are powerful parallels between them
and events in the lives of such pagan gods as,
say, Osiris, Attis or Odin, then it becomes
apparent that human beings have – in every
place and time – been saying the same thing
over and over and over again. Rather than
dissent, therefore, there is accord. Far from
undermining a living religion such as
Christianity, awareness of its shared imagery
and symbolism serves to enrich it and to give
credibility to the mythologies to which it
relates, for all touch on profound truths that
are not the property of any one belief system
alone. There is no need for argument, then, for
the Many are really the One.

MYTHIC ARCHETYPES

The grand archetypes of myth – those models
and patterns that recur again and again – can
in fact come to our aid in decoding some of
the symbols and more obscure messages of
contemporary religion. Instead of uprooting
such imagery and displaying it solely within
the confines of a single belief system,
replanting it in the landscape of its mythic
origins suddenly reveals a richer meaning, a
deeper significance, as if the sun has just
broken through the clouds to illuminate details
once lost in shadow, whose new clarity now

sends up new shoots every now and then, and
yet all the time remains largely unchanged,
save perhaps for a few minor adaptations
depending on the particular soil through which
it has to pass.

Monotheistic Christianity, for example, was
the next shoot along the runner from which
monotheistic Judaism sprouted – a shoot
which bore some remarkable resemblances to
other, older shoots that grew into the many
pantheistic mythologies originating in that
region of the world. There may be differences
between the message of these two living
religions and those of their pagan counterparts, but neither sprang fully formed from the
rock of the Middle East; they have their roots
in pagan soil, and have been influenced by this

contributes to a better understanding of the whole. It is all a matter of ways of seeing, of putting on, as it were, a different set of spectacles of perception.

Some of the most fascinating examples of how a knowledge of the symbolic language of myth can throw light on some of the more baffling images of religion relate to the Virgin Mary and the birth, death and resurrection of Christ. Born in a state of grace, without the taint of Original Sin that afflicts the rest of humanity, Mary goes on to conceive without having sexual intercourse. Innocent though she is, even she knows the physiological requirements for conception – 'How shall this be, seeing I know not a man? she challenges the Archangel Gabriel who has come to announce her forthcoming pregnancy. 'The Holy Ghost shall come upon thee, and the power of the Highest shall overshadow thee,' replies Gabriel smoothly, 'therefore that holy thing which shall be born of thee shall be called the Son of God.' (St Luke, 1:30–35)

Everything happens as the angel predicts, and Mary duly gives birth to the infant Jesus with her virginity still intact – a paradox that has puzzled and amused the rational, annoyed feminists, and even been rejected by some of the clergy. This is where pagan models can come to the rescue, for pagan religion abounds with images of such miraculous conceptions – of lone, virgin mothers and absent fathers. Over in Asia Minor, Nana, the earthly incarnation of the goddess Cybele, conceived Attis by eating a pomegranate or almond. In Ireland, the divine hero Cú Chulainn was said to be the son of the shining god Lugh, but the actual cause of his birth, the generative principle, was the mayfly swallowed by his mother Dechtire. In Britain, the goddess Cerridwen conceived the divine bard Taliesin after swallowing the single grain into which her servant boy, Gwion Bach, had transformed himself. Across the ocean in Mexico, Coatlicue conceived when touched by a ball of feathers that fell from the sky.

What all these mystical conceptions highlight is the changing view of female power and the feminine in the creative process. In the beginning, the goddess was all – she was the sole creatrix, the Virgin Mother; then, as male power began to assert itself, she took a lover by whom she became pregnant, but who still remained her subordinate – he was the part to her whole; finally, the tables were completely turned, and the god assumed the goddess's original power of sole creation, relegating her to the point of, in some world religions, total banishment.

The Virgin Mary stands midway along this continuum. Her virgin status and the mystical conception of her child look back to the image of the old Mother Goddess who created alone. Indeed, Mary's traditional costume of blue cloak and white gown unmask her, for these are the colours of wave and foam, recalling the limitless ocean of being, the primordial source of all things. The halo of stars she sometimes wears brings to mind her other title, Stella Maris, Star of the Sea, by which the goddesses Isis, Ishtar, Aphrodite and Venus were also known. *Mare*, the Latin word for 'sea', was another of Aphrodite's titles, and the name Mary has been similarly linked with *mare*. In a ceremony that literally brings myth alive, Mediterranean peoples still, probably unknowingly, honour Mary as Goddess of the Sea when they place an effigy of her in a small boat and bring her across the waters to greet the faithful, like some latter-day Aphrodite in her shell arising from the sea foam, or like the gorgeous Lakshmi of Hindu mythology,

churned up out of the ocean of milk and bobbing along in her lotus blossom.

Despite such divine precedents, Mary is forced to relinquish any claim to power by the new god Jehovah, who appears at the other end of the continuum and storms onto the stage, huffing and puffing and demanding total credit for the ability to procreate. In the Biblical picture, the old Virgin Goddess is reduced to no more than a passive vessel, the medium chosen by God to give physical form to spirit, in much the same way as a sculptor

BELOW: MOTHER EARTH GIVES BIRTH – A COYOTE, REPRESENTING THE EARTH, OPENS ITS JAWS TO RELEASE THE AZTEC GOD QUETZALCOATL. THE SHELLS FROM WHICH THE PIECE IS MADE MAY HAVE BEEN REMOVED FROM THE SHELL PALACE OF QUETZALCOATL IN TULA, MEXICO.

might choose wood or stone to flesh out an idea already in his head.

The child that Mary will bear is none other than the incarnation of God himself, and behind the veil of this story of the Virgin, God the Father and God the Son who died and was reborn, we again glimpse one of the grand archetypes of myth and pagan religion. Mary, as we have already seen, evokes the old goddess. In becoming the mother of God (the Son), she is effectively also the bride of God (the Father). Furthermore, God the Son goes on to die but is resurrected. What thus reveals itself here is the ancient and time-honoured pattern, familiar the length and breadth of the old world from at least as early as 5000 BC– that of the Goddess and her son-lover who dies and is reborn. The image is found, for example, in the myths of Inanna and Dumuzi and their Babylonian counterparts, Ishtar and Tammuz (see page 112), and in the Egyptian myths of Isis and Osiris (see page 116).

For good measure, Christ dies on a cross, thus reinforcing the link further, for the tree is another potent archetype. The body of Osiris is enclosed in a tamarisk tree; Attis dies on a pine tree (and similarly, like Christ, rises from the dead three days later); and then of course there are all those Trees of Life with which mythology is crammed – the apple tree of immortality tended by the Hesperides, for example, or the Tree in the midst of the Garden of Eden, around which twines the body of the Serpent of Regeneration.

MYTH AS HISTORY

As well as expressing spiritual truth, myth provides a time capsule of race memory, for in it is stored, in the form of allegory, a record of cultural change. Stories of the destruction of a 'monster' goddess by a god, such as the brutal killing of Tiamat by Marduk (see page 18), express in narrative picture language the kind of change from a matriarchal to a patriarchal system mentioned above. In less dramatic fashion, the domestic conflict between Hera and her philandering husband Zeus that features in so many classical Greek myths, in which Hera is presented as the stereotypical jealous wife seeking to undermine her husband's favourites, may also be illustrating the same point.

In Indo-European tradition, which includes numerous different mythologies from as far apart as India and Ireland, and similarly in the traditions of the Near East, the conquering male sky gods that rampaged their way into human consciousness several millenia ago were products of the minds of Aryan and Semitic nomadic warrior tribesmen. According to

RIGHT: ONE INDO-EUROPEAN HERO WITH NO TIME TO HANG AROUND – THESEUS ABANDONS ARIADNE ON THE ISLAND OF NAXOS, AFTER SHE HAS HELPED HIM IN HIS QUEST AGAINST THE MINOTAUR. FORTUNATELY, ARIADNE WAS LATER RESCUED FROM HER PLIGHT BY THE GOD DIONYSOS.

fear that these mounted warriors – half-man and half-horse – must have generated can only be imagined. The sight of them may have been the inspiration for the Greek centaur, that curious hybrid in which the upper body of a man grows out of the back of a horse, like some strange extra limb.

The imposition of the Aryan and Semitic world views on an earlier vision resulted in bodies of belief in which two contradictory mythic streams flowed. One – the Aryan-Semitic – focused on division, polarity, conquest, and separation from nature. The male gods of this system were emanant – they ruled the world from somewhere 'out there'. They were the tribal chieftains, the warlike gods of sky and storm – the club-wielding thunder god Thor of Norse myth, the mountaintop-dweller and lightning-thrower Zeus of Greece, the Persian Mithra who was *Sol Invictus*, the Unconquered Sun that vanquishes the darkness, as well as such hero figures as Perseus and Hercules, or Cú Chulainn of Celtic tradition.

The other, goddess-centred model offered a completely different view of the world. It was inclusive, saw all of existence as a harmonious whole, and perceived the immanence of the goddess in all things. It drew its inspiration from the cyclical rhythms of nature – the moon that endlessly waxes and wanes, the sea that ebbs and flows, the earth that burgeons and withers only to blossom once more. Since these phenomena contained within a single entity such apparent polar opposites as growth and decay, the goddess who personified them could do likewise, and this serves to explain her multiple personalities. The same goddess could therefore preside over both life and death, whereas in the divisive Aryan-Semitic model, death would be an adversary to be conquered or, alternatively, a once-and-for-all ending rather than a waiting state of formlessness before rebirth.

Sometimes the goddess adopted a dual personality to express the image of life and death as the two parts that made up the whole. Babylonian Ishtar, for example, the goddess of life, love and all that was vital, had a sister by

Marija Gimbutas, the late Professor of Archeology at the University of California (see Bibliography), the Aryans or Kurgans swept south and west from what were their homelands in the steppes between the Dnieper and Volga rivers. They came in three waves, Gimbutas believed, between 4300–2800 BC. The Semitic invaders, meanwhile, moved northward from the Syrian and Arabian deserts. By the time the Iron Age was established (c. 1250 BC in the Near East), the hierarchical, patriarchal mythology and warrior ethos of these two groups of invaders had been imposed on the agrarian, egalitarian, Neolithic and Bronze Age goddess cultures of the peoples whose territories they conquered.

One great advantage the Aryans, in particular, had over those they conquered was the horse, which they domesticated as early as 5000 BC and which allowed them to cover territory at hitherto unimaginable speeds. The

Kore transformed into Persephone, Queen of the Dead, for death and destruction. Destruction here, however, does not mean consignment to eternal oblivion, but rather a breaking-up of the form in order to reassemble its component parts into a new piece: in the goddess-centred world view, death is the precursor to life on the endlessly revolving wheel of existence, as the Persephone myth perfectly illustrates.

MYTH AND NATURE

As well as reflecting historical change, particular mythologies have also been coloured by the environments out of which they have grown. Compare, for example, Norse mythology with the mythologies of Greece or India. Although all three are branches from the same Indo-European stock, the former has a very different flavour from the latter two. Greek and Indian myths often reveal a sensuality that is in keeping with their geographic origins in lands of lazy heat and mellow fruitfulness where the living was generally easy. The Norse people, on the other hand, had to contend with a much less hospitable environment, of ice and snow, of long winters and short summers, and taken as a whole their mythology has the same harsh, uncompromising quality as the terrain and climate which gave it birth.

Although such mythologies gain much of their particular personality from their individual environments, a degree of separation from nature has already taken place. Natural phenomena have been personified as various deities, and therefore a split has begun to occur – the idea of divine emanance has taken root. In other, older mythologies, however, immanence still holds sway. Here, all of nature – every stone, every leaf, the water in every stream, the clouds in

the name of Erishkigal, who was queen of the dead (see page 112). Often, though, the goddess split herself into three to become the Triple Goddess, representing the unity of birth, life, and death. For example, Kali Ma of Indian mythology – who was most famous in her aspect as the terrifying, bloodthirsty goddess of death but who also enjoyed the title Jaganmata, the Mother of All Living as well as many other goddess names including Parvati, Lakshmi and Durga – was perceived as the Creator, Preserver and Destroyer, three functions which were later adopted by the Brahmans for their gods, Brahma, Vishnu and Shiva (Shiva was Kali's consort). Three colours represented her trinity: white for creation, red for preservation, and black for destruction.

In Greek myth, an example of the Triple Goddess in operation may be found in the story of Persephone (see page 120). Here, the maiden Kore stands for birth and creation, her mother Demeter for life and preservation, and the sky, the tiniest insect, the smallest grain of sand – is humming with the same connecting electrical current of creation, like minute nuclei in some vast, oscillating whole. This way of seeing the world is known as animism, and it underpins what may be regarded as the most ancient belief systems in the world.

Because everything in animistic belief – whether tangible or intangible, animate or inanimate – is just one manifestation of the same source of being, it follows that these outward forms can easily change. What appears to be a human being one moment can, the next instant, be a bird, or a clump of reeds, or a swirl of mist – these are the classic shape-shifting practices of the shaman of animistic religion. The belief that everything is part of one whole also means that everything is sacred and not to be harmed – a holistic view of the world that is increasingly appealing in our contemporary age with its growing awareness of environmental issues.

The mythologies of such 'primitive' peoples as the Maoris and Native Americans have a strong streak of animism, which produces stories of particular sensitivity and beauty. (See, for example, *Sky Spirit and Fine Weather Woman* on page 60.)

IN REMEMBRANCE

The myths told in this book, therefore, and all the hundreds of others for which there could never be enough space, are not quaint, fanciful stories to be dismissed and consigned to the scrap heap of outmoded knowledge. They are a treasure hoard of wisdom, of compassion, of beauty, a triumph of the creative imagination, a journey into the landscape of the soul. They are balm for the spirit, and a peephole into the glory of paradise. They are our heritage, saved for us at first by generations of bards and storytellers who kept the oral tradition alive, and subsequently by poets, folklorists and historians who thought the stories worth recording for posterity. When reading them, then, remember all those before you, in some cases going back over literally thousands of years, who have taken the trouble to preserve these ancient stories for your present pleasure.

As this version of an Armenian saying so elegantly puts it:

Three golden apples fell from heaven:
one for those who told the story,
one for those who heard it,
and one for all the countless many
who have cared enough to remember ...

... so catch your apple, eat, and enjoy.

BELOW: ULYSSES' OWN STORY OF ADVENTURE – HIS SHIP PASSES THE SIRENS IN A FRESCO BY ALLORI ALESSANDRO (1535–1607).

This Babylonian creation myth comes from 'The Epic of Creation', and features Marduk, a new mythic role model from the Semitic and Indo-European repertoire, that of the warrior sky god whose weapons are storm, lightning and thunderbolt, and who rides the heavens like the whirlwind.

DIVIDING THE WATERS

In the beginning, there was only Apsu, the primordial ocean, and Tiamat, the tumultuous sea. From the mingling of their waters came three generations of gods – Mummu, spirit of the waves, and the serpents Lakhmu and Lakhamu, who in their turn produced Anshar and Kishar, to whom in turn were born Anu, Ea, and the deities of sky, earth and under-earth. In this way three generations of gods were created.

But these new gods were noisy and trouble-some, and Apsu could find no repose.

'By day I cannot rest, by night I cannot sleep,' Apsu complained to his wife Tiamat. 'Let us rid ourselves of this tiresome brood.'

Tiamat was outraged at such a suggestion. 'How can we destroy what we ourselves have created?' she demanded angrily.

So Apsu turned to Mummu instead, and with him hatched a secret plan to kill the new gods. But Ea – who knows all things and sees all things – divined Apsu's intention and, with magical incantations, made Apsu and Mummu prisoner. He took Apsu's crown from his head, stole his glory for himself, slew him, and built his palace on his back.

Tiamat now turned her anger on Ea. She was roused to battle fury, and it was a terrible sight to see. The great all-mother, alone and unaided, brought forth from her body all manner of monsters – enormous serpents with sharp fangs and blood that was poison;

RIGHT: A *KUDDURRU* – A CHARTER FOR A GRANT OF LAND – OF THE BABYLONIAN KING MARDUK-ZAKIR-SHUMI, FROM THE LATE ASSYRIAN PERIOD, C. 850 BC.
PAGE 16: THE TRINITY – SIVA, BRAHMA AND VISHNU, STONE LINTEL, 12TH CENTURY.

dragons with glittering scales; scorpion-men; fish-men; storm demons; wild dogs – until at last eleven different species of monster stood before her. Surrounded by this terrifying host and a company of loyal gods, she set off to do battle with her offspring.

When the gods saw the goddess and her army closing in, they trembled with terror and all fell silent. Anshar sent Anu, his eldest son, against her. But Anu had not the courage to withstand her, and returned. His brother Ea fared no better, so Ea at last called his son Marduk to him.

'My son,' he said, 'the gods face annihilation at the hands of our mother Tiamat. It has fallen to you save us. Go before Anshar and tell him what you will do.'

So Marduk presented himself before Anshar. But one good deed deserves another, and in return for slaying Tiamat, Marduk demanded that he be given dominion over all the gods; from henceforth, it was he that would determine their fate, and whatever he created would remain without change.

The bargain was struck, and the gods conferred on Marduk the sceptre, the throne, the royal ring, and the thunderbolt. Marduk made a net to entangle the enemy and collected together all his weapons – the lightning, the hurricane, and the winds from the four corners of the earth. Then he mounted his storm chariot, drawn by the steeds Killer, Pitiless, Trampler, and Flier, and roared off to do battle with Tiamat. 'May the winds carry her blood to secret places!' the gods called after him.

When Tiamat saw Marduk, she opened her mouth to swallow him, but Marduk let fly an evil wind, and the wind filled the mouth of the all-mother, and poured into her belly. Then Marduk let fly an arrow that tore into her inner parts and split her heart. Tiamat fell lifeless before him. The gods and monsters who were with her tried to flee, but Marduk caught them in his net and made them prisoner.

Triumphant on the corpse of Tiamat, Marduk smashed her skull and slashed her arteries so that her blood gushed out and was borne by the winds to secret places. Then he split her body from top to tail, and set one half above to form the firmament of heaven, and the other half below to form the earth. He placed the heavenly bodies in the sky, setting their courses, fixed the length of the year, and fashioned mankind to fill the earth.

A NEW ORDER

This tale, in which the brutal killing of Tiamat is so relished, is, like so many myths, an allegory of change. Tiamat – the mother – represents the old matriarchal order, overcome by a new patriarchy, exemplified here by the avenger Marduk. Tiamat – 'The Deep' – is linked etymologically to 'tehom', 'The Deep', of the 'Genesis' creation story, in which Jehovah – another sky god – similarly breathes on 'the face of the waters' and separates the 'waters above' from the 'waters below'. However, by the time we reach 'Genesis', the goddess who was formerly the personification of the primordial sea and from whose physical body the world was made has been reduced to an abstract concept, and the power of procreation is now in the hands of a male god alone.

Featuring the same imagery found in other creation myths of Indo-European stock, this story has, however, its own particular Nordic flavour reflecting the harsh Icelandic environment in which it was fashioned. The shifts in detail which occur imply a piecing together of different versions of an original tale – for example, the Land of Ice begins in the north 'above' and ends in the south 'below', while the Land of Fire present at the start is excluded from the final nine worlds – so matters of geography and logic are best ignored when reading the story.

FIRE AND ICE

Fire melts ice and ice quenches fire and in this way the world was made, so the Norsemen relate, in a tale told by father to son and mother to daughter, a tale of such ancient knowing that all have long since forgotten when it was first remembered.

In the beginning, so the story tells, there was neither land nor sea nor sky, only a vast chasm of emptiness called Ginnungagap. Slowly, in the region north of Ginnungagap clouds and shadows and freezing mists began to form and they swirled in the emptiness like ghosts of the dawn. And in the coldness of the north the vapours froze and turned into vast sheets of snow and ice, and in the middle a spring sprang up, called Hvergelmir, and from it twelve rivers flowed. This was how Niflheim, the Land of Ice, was made.

Meanwhile in the heat of the region south

LEFT: ALLFATHER ODIN SEATED ON HIS THRONE. ODIN WAS ONE OF THE OLDEST GODS OF THE NORSE PANTHEON, AND WITH HIS BROTHERS FASHIONED THE EARTH, THE SKY AND THE SEA FROM THE BONES, BODY AND BLOOD OF THE GIANT YMIR.

of Ginnungagap, sparks of flame were fanned into being, pinpricks of light that danced and darted in the blackness and came together to create one seething, frothing, all-consuming sea of fire. This was how Muspell, the Land of Fire, was made.

Yet still there was a void between the two lands, and the rivers from Hvergelmir, whose waters were bitter poison, flowed into the void and the poison in them congealed into crusts of ice, and the vapour that rose from the rivers settled and froze into hoar-frost, so that in the end the whole northern half of Ginnungagap was caked in layers of ice and rime, and a more dismal and desolate place has never been. In the southern half, meanwhile, Ginnungagap glowed and burned with the heat from the furnace of Muspell.

A GIANT COMES FROM THE ICE

Fire melts ice and ice quenches fire, and in the middle of Ginnungagap was a place that was neither biting cold nor searing hot but mild and gentle as a summer's day. Here warm breezes from the south caressed the ice from the north as a minstrel strokes the strings of his harp, and under their soft touch the ice began to yield its hardness and to melt, and in the first trickling drops of melted ice the seeds of life stirred.

Like raindrops that fall from the roof and collect in a puddle on the ground, so the drops of melted snow and ice ran together and swelled and moved and grew and began to take on a shape, and you would have known it for what it was if only you had been there to see, for it was the shape of a gigantic man. And the giant rose up and stretched his giant limbs as if he had just woken from a deep slumber and placed his giant foot on the ice and turned his giant head all around to view the world through his giant eyes, and the giant's name was Ymir.

One day, while Ymir lay sleeping, a profuse sweat broke out all over his body and out of the dew of the sweat of his left armpit were born a man and a woman, giants both like Ymir, and so it was that Ymir became father to the race of frost giants.

A COW COMES FROM THE ICE

Fire melts ice and ice quenches fire, and as the heat from the south continued to thaw the snow from the north, the water from the melting ice took another form, this time that of a cow, whose name was Audumla. Audumla fed on the salt in the ice, and Ymir fed on the four rivers of milk that flowed from Audumla's generous udders.

And as Audumla was licking away the ice with the rasp of her hot, rough tongue, the hair of a man emerged; she licked some more, and his head appeared; she licked some more, and his whole body was freed. His name was Buri, and in time he had a son named Bor, and Bor married Bestla, a daughter of one of the frost giants, and Bor and Bestla produced three sons – Odin, who would be the father of the gods, Vili, and Ve. And so it was that gods came into being, half-giant and half-man.

THE THREE GODS MAKE THE EARTH

As time went on, the sons of Bor conceived a hatred for the frost giants with their rough, unruly ways, and a great conflict ensued in which Ymir was slaughtered, and there was so much blood in his body that it gushed out like a tidal wave and flooded Ginnungagap, drowning all the frost giants save Bergelmir and his wife, who escaped in a small boat on the swell of the hot and frothing red tide. It was from this pair that the new generation of giants would come.

Then Odin, Vili and Ve carried the body of Ymir to the middle of Ginnungagap, and from it fashioned the world, and no part of the giant's body was wasted. From his flesh they made the soil; from his unbroken bones the mountains; from his shattered ones the rocks and the stones. From his skull they made the sky, from his brains the clouds, and from his blood the ocean which they poured in a great ring around the world.

THE GODS FIX STARS IN THE SKY

But the work of creation was not yet finished, and many more wonders were still to come.

Odin, Vili and Ve took the darting sparks of flame and burning embers from Muspell and

placed them in the sky to become the sun and moon and stars, giving some fixed places in the firmament and appointing for others a set course to follow. Then Odin took the dark-skinned, dark-eyed, dark-haired giantess whose name was Night, and her son, fair-haired and shining-faced Day, and gave them chariots in which to ride around the sky. In the sky were wolves, too: there was the wolf that chases the Moon in order to swallow it, called Hati, and behind him came Skoll, who wishes to swallow the Sun and who will one day succeed in his desire.

Under the earth, at each of the four corners, Odin stationed one of the dwarves that the three gods had made from the maggots that fed on the corpse of Ymir, and who now live under the hills and in the hollow places of the earth. The names of these four dwarves were North, South, East and West.

And in the ocean that circled the earth, that was so wide that no man would dare to cross it, floated Jormungand, the terrible world serpent who was so long that he could wrap himself around the world and take his tail in his mouth.

THE GODS MAKE THE FIRST MORTALS

But the work of creation was not yet finished, and many more wonders were still to come.

One day, as Odin and his companions were walking along the shore where the sea meets the land, they came upon two fallen trees, one an ash and the other an elm. And they took the two trees, and Odin breathed into them the breath of life, Vili gave them hearts and souls and the power of thought, and Ve gave them ears to hear and eyes to see, and thus from two lifeless trees came the first mortal man and woman, whose names were Ask and Embla.

So that Ask and Embla and all their descendants might live in peace and happiness, Odin, Vili and Ve took the eyebrows of Ymir and laid them down to make a vast enclosure in the middle of the world that was called Midgard or Middle Earth, and it was here that Ask and

Embla settled, and it was here, too, that mankind has lived ever since.

But the gods did not forget that they, too, needed a home, so they created Asgard that lay high above Midgard and was linked to it by Bifröst, the bridge of fire that men call the rainbow, which was made from three colours with great magic and skill.

THE GODS GIVE ORDER TO CREATION

And when the gods had finished all their busy work, they had ordered creation into nine worlds that lay on three levels, above, below and beneath.

Above were Asgard, home of Odin and his warrior offspring the Aesir; Vanaheim, home of the gods known as the Vanir; and Alfheim, the 'elf-home' of the light elves.

Below were Midgard, home of man, and Jotunheim, home of the giants. Here, too, were the homes of the dwarves and the dark elves – Nidavellir the 'dark home' and Svartalfheim the 'black elf home'.

Beneath the worlds of the gods, the giants, the elves and men were the last worlds of all – Niflheim and Hel, the homes of the dead.

And surrounding and upholding and permeating the whole work of creation – as a wooden framework bears the weight and form of a house – was Yggdrasil, the mighty ash tree that stands with one root in Niflheim by the spring of Hvergelmir; one in Jotunheim by Mimir the Spring of Wisdom; and one in Asgard by the Well of Fate that is watched over by the Norns, those three ancient sisters of weird in whose gift lie the fortunes of both gods and of men.

This is how the world was made, in the old, old tale told by the Norsemen ... and this is my tale as I have told it to you.

THE AXIS MUNDI

With its trunk running up through the centre of the universe, Yggdrasil may be regarded as the 'axis mundi', literally the axis, or pivot, of the world. Yggdrasil was one of several world trees. The Asvattha tree of Hindu mythology, for example, performed a similar task to Yggdrasil, except that it was inverted, with its roots in the sky and its branches spreading out over the earth, thus expressing the idea that the creative force comes down from above. In Islamic tradition, the Tree of Happiness likewise buried its roots in the farthest heaven and stretched its canopy of branches over the world.

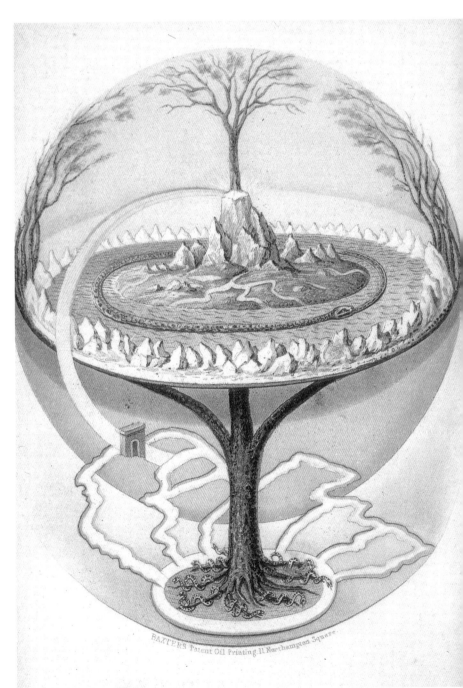

BAXTERS Patent Oil Printing 11 Northampton Square

FISHING UP THE WORLD

This famous creation story features Maui, the arch-trickster of Polynesian myth. The trickster is a classic figure in the pantheon of many mythologies – a character who is for ever up to mischief and has the power to change his shape to do so. However, unlike some of his counterparts such as Loki (see page 40), Maui is not darkly malevolent, but rather anarchic and subversive.

There were once six brothers who all went by the name of Maui. There was Maui-mua, Maui-taha, Maui-roto, Maui-waho, Maui-pae, and Maui-tikitiki-o-Taranga. Now the youngest of these brothers was different from the others, as youngest brothers often are. For one thing, there was the curious business of his birth. Aborted early from his mother's womb while barely more than a germ of life, he was cared for by the sea people and lived with them until he was of an age to rejoin his own kind.

Strange beginnings make strange endings, and it may be the unnatural manner of his birth that accounts for his unmanly preference for his mother rather than his father, and for his mischievous, disrespectful ways.

ABOVE: MAUI ON THE POINT OF LANDING HIS GREATEST CATCH – THE FISH THAT HE PULLS UP WILL BECOME THE NORTH ISLAND OF NEW ZEALAND.

Maui was also lazy. While his brothers were out fishing in their *waka*, he lay about the house, idling the day away in the most pleasurable manner imaginable.

'Can't you see how hard your brothers work?' his wives berated him. 'Just look at you, lying there like that! It's a disgrace. Now get up and go to work like a man!'

This tiresome and unreasonable complaining began to grate on Maui's ears. Even if it meant getting seasick and soaked, a day out in his brothers' boat must surely be more restful than staying at home, listening to his wives' nagging. He stirred himself, left the house, and went to the cave where the bones of his ancestor, Murirangawhenua, lay buried. And here he did a terrible thing. He took the jawbone of Murirangawhenua as his fishing hook, an act so defiant of all that is sacred that it risked the most severe consequences. But Maui must have been especially blessed, for nothing ill befell him – indeed, the theft seemed to bring him luck, as we shall soon see.

If Maui's wives did not want him in the house, his brothers, fearing his pranks, certainly did not want him in their boat. So, taking the form of a tiny shrimp, he hid in the waka and waited until they were out at sea.

When the brothers had set anchor, Maui resumed his normal shape and sprang forth from his hiding place. Enraged that he had outwitted them in this way, the brothers refused to give him any bait, but Maui hit himself on the nose until it bled, and smeared the jawbone-hook with his own blood, as bait.

He lowered his line with its bloodied hook over the side of the boat. Down, deep down it went until it could sink no farther for it had reached the very bottom of the ocean. No sooner had it touched the seabed than Maui felt a powerful tug. He gripped the line tight. The waters began to churn and swirl, the waves reared up above the waka and tossed it about and spun it around as if it were a child's plaything, a boat of folded paper.

'Let the line go!' screamed the terrified brothers, 'Do you want to kill us all?'

But Maui would not let go. Pulling on the line with all his strength – and he was very strong – he sang a magical song that soared like an eagle above the storm, and out of the boiling, bubbling sea there came a shape, a giant fish of such vastness as human eyes have never seen before nor since. At last, all of the great creature, lured by blood and bone from

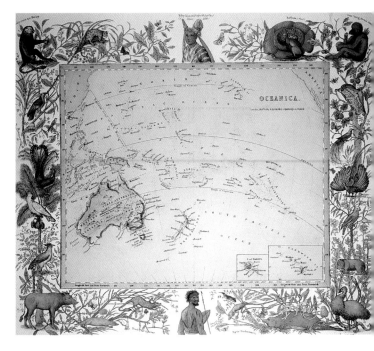

ABOVE: IN THE VAST EXPANSE OF THE PACIFIC, AS SHOWN IN THIS 19TH-CENTURY MAP, MAUI'S 'FISH' FLOATS EAST OF AUSTRALIA.

its home at the bottom of the ocean, lay spread out on the surface of the sea.

Now that he had made his catch, Maui swam for the shore to make offerings of thanks to the gods, instructing his brothers not to touch the great fish until his return. But as soon as he was out of sight, the greedy brothers began to hack and cut at the fish in order to share it among themselves, causing the creature to writhe and turn and twist in the throes of its death.

Whatever the reason may be, Maui never did come back for his catch, for the great fish lies floating in the same place still, as you yourself would see if you happened to gaze out over the South Pacific. His body is old and cold and hard, shaped into mountains and cliffs and valleys by the writhings and turnings and twistings of his dying moments. He is Te Ika-a-Maui, Maui's Fish, the land that white men call the North Island of New Zealand. And if you were to look a little farther to South Island, you would see there Maui's *waka*, the boat from which he cast his magic hook and first fished up the land.

MONSTERS OF THE DEEP

In many mythologies, the ocean symbolizes the watery 'womb' of the ancient Mother Goddess out of which creation comes, and the inhabitant of these waters – the fish or sea creature – is therefore her manifestation. One famous example of this archetypal Monster of the Deep is Leviathan, the sea serpent of the Old Testament, a personification of the Goddess demonized by the new patriarchal religion headed by Yahweh (Jehovah). Like Maui's fish or the Babylonian Tiamat (see page 18), she dies a brutal death at male hands:

'In that day the Lord with his sore and great and strong sword shall punish Leviathan the piercing serpent, even Leviathan that crooked serpent; and he shall slay the dragon that is in the sea.' (Isaiah 27: 1)

Based on oral legends from the Shinto tradition, this Japanese myth was among many recorded in various texts including the 'Kojiki' and the 'Nihongi'. Completed in AD 712, the 'Kojiki' was commissioned by the Empress Gemmyo (AD 707–715) from the scribe O no Yasumaro. During the reign of Emperor Gensho (AD 715–726), he then went on, with Prince Toneri, to compile the 'Nihongi', a history of Japan, the first part of which – the 'Jindaiki', the 'record of the age of gods' – provided all the different versions of the myths which then existed. It was presented to the Emperor in AD 720.

IZANAGI AND IZANAMI

RIGHT: ACCOMPANIED BY IZANAMI, IZANAGI PREPARES TO DIP THE MAGICAL SPEAR INTO THE SEA OF CHAOS, AND THUS CREATE THE ISLANDS OF JAPAN.

In the chaos before the beginning, three illustrious but invisible beings formed themselves on the Plain of Heaven. They were Ame-No-Minaka-Nushi-No-Kami, Taka-Mi-Musubi-No-Kami, and Kami-Musubi-No-Kami. After them came more generations of gods, and the last of these were Izanagi and Izanami, brother and sister to each other.

At this time, the earth was still young and formless – a bed of reeds that floated, like a pool of oil, like a drifting jelly-fish, on the primordial sea. The gods chose Izanagi and Izanami to give form to this floating world, and to aid them in their task, they provided them with a magical jewelled spear.

Izanagi and Izanami took the spear and,

LEFT: 'FULL MOON AT SEBA' BY HIROSHIGE. TSUKI-YOMI, GOD OF THE MOON, CAME FROM THE RIGHT EYE OF IZANAGI.
BELOW LEFT: THE 'WEDDED ROCKS' IN ISE BAY ARE SAID TO HAVE SHELTERED IZANAGI AND IZANAMI.

standing on the Floating Bridge of Heaven, they dipped it into the sea and began to stir. In the place where they stirred, the waters started to coagulate and glistening crystals formed. When they lifted the spear, the few drops of brine that fell from it became the first dry land. This was the island of Onokoro, which means 'naturally coagulated'.

Izanagi and Izanami descended to the island and there came together as man and wife to create the other islands of Japan, and to beget the gods who rule the natural world. From Izanami's womb came the god of wind, the god of mountains, the god of trees, and other divine beings. But it was the birth of Hi-No-Kagu-Tsuchi, god of fire, that brought her end for his passage into the world was so fiery that he burned her body and she died.

Izanami descended to Yomi, the underworld of the dead, while Izanagi lamented his loss, weeping so copiously that his tears became the goddess Moaning-river.

When all his tears were spent, Izanagi determined to journey to Yomi to bring back his wife. Izanami met him at the entrance to Yomi but told him that she could not return with him for she had already eaten the food of the underworld. She begged him not to enter the realm of the dead, nor to look on her there, but Izanagi would not listen. He broke off a tooth from his comb, lit it as a torch and followed her inside. What he saw made him gasp in horror – instead of the wife he remembered, Izanami revealed herself as a corpse, decomposing and devoured by worms, watched over by the Eight Thunders that had sprung from her body when she died.

Humiliated and betrayed at being seen in this form, Izanami loosed the demons of the underworld after her husband. Pursued by the Hags of Hell, the Eight Thunders and finally the Soldiers of Hell, Izanagi fled as fast as he could, defending himself by magical means. When at last he reached the gate to the upper world, he picked three peaches, threw them at the demon soldiers, and so managed to make good his escape.

To cleanse himself of the contamination of the world of the dead, Izanagi plunged into the cool, refreshing waters of the sea. He washed his left eye, and from it came Amaterasu, the Goddess of the Sun, to whom he gave the Plain of Heaven. He washed his right eye, and from it came Tsuki-Yomi, the God of the Moon, to whom he gave the Kingdom of Night. He washed his nose, and from it came Susano-Wo, the God of Storms, to whom he gave the Plain of the Seas.

Izanagi continued in the realm of the living, while Izanami became a goddess of the dead, and from that time until the ending of time, the pair have agreed to be forever parted.

In contrast to other traditions of Indo-European origin in which the earth is seen as quintessentially female and the sky male – a view which still remains so deeply imbedded in contemporary Western consciousness that we do not even stop to question it – this ancient Egyptian myth switches the genders, making the heavens female and the land male.

THE PARTING OF HEAVEN AND EARTH

In Nun, the great sea of nothingness that existed before the beginning, lay the spirit of Atum-Ra, and in Atum-Ra lay the seed of all life to come. When he had manifested himself from out of the sea of nothingness, Atum-Ra reached into himself and drew out Shu, the air, and Tefnut, who was the dew and the rain. And air and rain came together as husband and wife to produce a son and a daughter, Geb and Nut, who became husband and wife in their turn, and things would have continued in this fashion, as you can well imagine, with brother and sister begetting brother and sister, had Atum-Ra not stepped in and changed the course of creation.

Seeing Nut and Geb lying together, as close as the twin halves of a walnut shell, Atum-Ra had one wish, and that was to separate them. Why this should be so none can say for sure; it may be that their union did not have his blessing; it may be that he wanted Nut for himself. What is sure is that he chose Shu to do his bidding, to prise the couple apart. Shu obeyed, and roughly and violently separated the pair, raising Nut up and pushing her belly and her breast so that they arched high above his head, held aloft by his outstretched arms, while Geb was left lying below. Nut's feet touched Geb's feet, her hands were by his head, and the great curve of her body covered his, as an upturned cup covers a saucer. In this way, the vault of heaven was separated from the land, and the space between them filled by the presence of Shu, as the air fills all empty spaces.

But this is not the end of the story of Geb and Nut, for Atum-Ra placed a curse on Nut, that she might not bear children on any day in any month of the year, and in this way he

ABOVE: AS WELL AS PERSONIFYING THE SKY, NUT WAS ALSO THE PROTECTRESS OF THE DEAD. THIS DETAIL FROM A COFFIN SHOWS HER WITH OUTSPREAD WINGS READY TO RECEIVE AND TAKE THEIR SOULS TO HER BOSOM, WHERE THEY WOULD BECOME THE STARS ON THE CELESTIAL VAULT OF HER BODY.

sought to keep her a prisoner of time, and to command her every moment.

But wise and compassionate Thoth, another of the gods, took pity on Nut and devised a plan to help her. He challenged the Moon to a game of draughts, and in the course of several games, he won for himself just a fraction – no more than a seventy-second part, but this was all that was needed – of the Moon's silver light, and from this light he fashioned five extra days. And he added these days to the three hundred and sixty that already made up the year, and because these were new days, not old, they were beyond the power of Atum-Ra to command.

On the five extra days that Thoth made, Nut and Geb joined together again, freely and joyously, and for each of those days Nut bore a child. Her first was Osiris, lord of life and fertility; her second was falcon-headed Horus; her third was white-skinned, red-haired Set, lord of the drought and the desert; her fourth was the great goddess Isis; and her fifth was Nephthys, Queen of the Dead. Isis married Osiris and Nephthys married Set and there was love and hatred, loyalty and betrayal, rivalry and murder … but all that, as they say, is another story.

WHAT'S IN A NAME?

The Egyptian pantheon is one of labyrinthine complexity, and this is hardly surprising since there was plenty of opportunity, given the timespan of Egyptian culture, for the identity and attributes of one deity to become merged or confused with those of another. There were, for example, up to twenty different deities by the name of Horus. The Horus of this story (Haroeris in Greek, Har Wer in Egyptian) has a solar character – he is the falcon that soars in the sky, whose eyes are the sun and moon respectively – and he was, initially at least, distinguished from Harsiesis or Hor-sa-iset, Horus son of Isis who avenges the murder of his father, Osiris. Similarly, Atum, the ancestor-creator, was strongly identified with Ra, another personification of the sun, who may be Nut's father/grandfather, or her husband, or her son. As her son, Ra is born each morning from her womb – as the sun is daily 'born' from the sky – and it was he who attached to her belly the stars that we see in the night sky.

BELOW: A PAPYRUS FROM THE 21ST DYNASTY, 1040–959 BC, SHOWS GEB AND NUT FORCIBLY SEPARATED, NEB LYING BELOW TO FORM THE EARTH, WHILE NUT ARCHES OVER HIM TO BECOME THE CELESTIAL VAULT, WITH HER TOES AND FINGERS TOUCHING THE 'ENDS OF THE EARTH'.

OLD SPIDER AND THE CLAM SHELL

This story comes from the Polynesian island of Nauru. As in so many other creation myths, in the beginning there is only a vast, formless ocean, and it is the creator's task to fashion the first land and place it in this watery environment. Note how the sky, made here from the upper half of a clam's shell, is envisaged as a 'dome', a common image – see, for example, the Norse version in which the sky is made from a giant's skull (page 21). In many cultures, too, the spider is an autonomous determining force, for she represents Fate who spins the Thread of Destiny, so her inititiating role is highly appropriate here.

Before the sun and the moon and the land were made, there was nothing but sea and a vast emptiness above, and in this vast emptiness floated Old Spider.

One day, looking down from her lofty position in space, Old Spider saw a giant clam shell, drifting on the sea. She reached down and examined the curious object to see if she could open it, but she could not, so she tapped it to see what was inside, and the shell made a hollow sound. Old Spider chanted a magic charm over the shell and the two halves of the shell parted like the unfurling of a flower bud, and Old Spider slipped inside.

Inside the shell all was dark as pitch for there was no sun or moon to light it. It was cramped, too, so that Old Spider could not stand up and had to bend herself double to fit into the small space in which she found herself. She began to explore the interior and, feeling her way in the dark, she at last came upon a smooth, rounded object with a coil-like form – it was a snail.

She took the snail, and, in order that some of her magical power might pass into it, she placed it under her arm and slept with it there for three days. After this time, she set it free to wend its slimy way. Then she hunted around the interior of the clam shell once more, and this time she found another snail, even bigger than the first, and she treated it in the same way. Then she turned to the first snail, who had not gone far for, as you know, snails are very slow, and she asked it:

'Can you make this room a little bigger so that we can stand up?'

The snail said it could, and no sooner said than done. The halves of the clam shell parted just enough to allow Old Spider to stretch her legs at last.

But it was still very dark inside the shell, so Old Spider took the first snail and set it in the upper half-shell of the clam, and made it into the moon, setting it in the place where the moon rises. Now there was a little silvery light to see by, and in this light Old Spider saw a large worm.

She asked the worm the same question she had asked the snail:

'Can you make this room a little bigger so that we can stand up?'

The worm said it could, and no sooner commanded than began. With all the strength of his mighty body, the worm pushed and stretched and heaved until gradually, bit by bit and with a good deal of creaking and groaning in the joints and sockets of the shell, he had prised the halves wide open. The upper half, raised high above his head, became the sky. The lower half became the land. The effort of this work caused the worm to sweat profusely, and his salty sweat ran from his body and collected in the lower shell, where it became the saltwater sea. At last, with his task accomplished, the worm felt his strength ebbing away from him and he lay down and died.

Now sky and moon, sea and land were formed, but there was still one thing wanting, and that was the sun. So Old Spider took the second snail, the one that was larger than the first, and placed it in the east of the sky, in the place where the dawn first comes, and it became the sun that lights the day.

And this is how, so the people of the islands tell, Old Spider made the world from a clam shell, many, many years ago.

THE SPINNING GODDESS

Sitting at the hub of her web and producing her silken skeins from the very fabric of her own body, the spider epitomizes the Spinning Goddess who spins the Thread of Destiny on the Wheel of Fortune. Such a powerful and creative role proves the Spinning Goddess to be immeasurably ancient. In Celtic, Norse, Greek and Mayan mythologies, she is the Great Mother, who exists outside of time and space, like Old Spider in this story. She often reproduces herself in triplicate, appearing as the three Fates, the weird sisters or the mystical Three-in-One.

Like so many creation myths, this Iroquois story presents the archetype of the world emerging from water. This particular tale has much in common with an Algonquian version of the creation (see page 34). Both are from the same general geographic region – northeastern North America – and both have the muskrat as the saviour of the day, the messenger who finds and delivers the raw material of creation – the small clump of soil that grows to form the earth as we know it.

THE TURTLE'S SHELL

In the beginning, there was no land, only a wide, wide water that stretched as far as the far horizons in every direction. This watery world was not without life, for in it lived such creatures as the muskrat, with its webbed feet and flat tail, and its cousin the thick-furred beaver who builds log lodges in which to live and house its young, and the otter who slides through the water like a snake. There were salmon and other fish, too, and birds – ducks with speckled and iridescent plumage and gaggles of cackling geese and diving birds with stick-like legs and pointed beaks.

But in this watery world there were no people and this is how, so the old story goes, mankind first came into the world.

Up in heaven, the Great Mother Aataensic conceived in her womb the first man and the first woman. Time passed, and soon, she knew, the moment would come when she should be delivered of her children. But one day, as she was walking about in heaven, she tripped and stumbled and fell, and came tumbling, tumbling, spiralling and turning, like a feather twirling on the breeze, all the

LEFT: THE BEAVER WAS ONE OF THE ANIMALS THAT INHABITED THE EARTH BEFORE THE BIRTH OF THE FIRST PEOPLE. WHEN IT SAW THE MOTHER GODDESS AATAENSIC COME TUMBLING OUT OF THE SKY, IT TRIED, UNSUCCESSFULLY, TO BREAK HER FALL.

way down through the limitless blue sky towards the wide, wide water below.

And as the animals looked up they saw Aataensic coming towards them, ever closer, and they went scurrying hither and thither to find a piece of earth that they could place under her to break her fall, for they did not want her to drown. The otter searched, the beaver searched, the ducks, the geese, the salmon and all the other creatures searched, but in the end it was the muskrat who found a clump of earth – not much bigger than a fist – and quickly placed it on the back of the turtle who was swimming through the water in his usual unhurried and ponderous way – and only just in time, too. For at that very moment, the Great Mother landed – with a gentle bounce – on the little piece of earth that had been placed for her on the turtle's back, and it was just enough to cushion her fall for her landing was as soft as if she had been dropped into a featherbed. It was here that she was delivered of the first man and the first woman and it is their children and their children's children who are all the people of the world.

Above: The turtle carries the world on its back. The idea of the earth being supported on the back of some giant animal, such as a turtle or elephant, is common in many ancient mythologies.

And as for the clump of earth, that was no bigger than a fist, a very strange thing began to happen, and you would have marvelled greatly if you had been there to see. The clump began to swell and grow and to spread out over the wide, wide water until it became an island and then a vast land that stretched north, south, east and west, with hills and valleys and forests and rivers. It became the earth on which we walk, and because it still rests on the turtle's shell, the people call it Turtle Island.

And so it is, when the sea is churned into a great swell of waves, that the people say the turtle is stirring.

And so it is, when the earth is shaken by tremors and rumblings and quakes, that the people say the turtle is stretching its limbs.

This Native American tale comes from the tradition of the Algonquian Indians of northeastern North America. While the Flood motif is common to many different cultures, the detail of sending out three emissaries to find signs of dry land is very reminiscent of Noah's actions in the Biblical Flood story, and suggests possible editorial tinkering with an indigenous idea, under the influence of the new Christian settlers from Europe.

MICHABO AND THE FLOOD

One day Michabo, lord of the east wind, was out hunting with his wolves when they came to a vast lake. Stirred by the excitement of the chase, the pack would not be turned from their course and plunged headlong into the water. But the lake was deep and it was not long before all the beasts had been swallowed up, leaving behind them no more than a few lingering ripples on the treacherously calm face of the water.

Coming close after them, Michabo saw what had befallen his beasts so he waded out into the lake to try to rescue them, pitting all his great strength against the water that slowed his path, to go ever deeper towards the middle. But so powerful was the movement of his limbs and so wild the swirling of his breath that the lake was stirred to a storm. Waves lashed the shore and the water rose higher and higher

ABOVE: A STORY LANDSCAPE — DAWN ON LAKE SUPERIOR IN THE GREAT LAKES REGION EVOKES THE VAST LAKE IN THIS TALE THAT BURST ITS BANKS AND FLOODED THE WORLD.

until it overflowed its banks and roared in turbulent torrents over the land, carrying with it stones and rocks and stripping the trees of all their branches.

When the flood finally abated and all was peaceful once more, the whole world had disappeared beneath a blanket of shining water that stretched east, west, north and south, as far as the farthest horizons.

Try as he might, nowhere could Michabo see one single spot of dry land. So he resolved to make a new world from the remains of the

OMNIPRESENT SPIRIT

Michabo's invisible presence could be detected in many natural phenomena – in the east wind, in the lightning, and in the swirling mists and cloud, for these were the smoke from his pipe. Although he is known as the 'Great Hare', the root from which his name derives means 'the light of the dawn' – an image which further reinforces his position as a powerful elemental spirit, present in the most fundamental aspects of nature.

THE DELUGE

The most famous of the world floods is, of course, that survived by Noah in the Old Testament. The Deluge, however, is by no means unique to Hebrew myth; it is a universal mythological theme. In ancient Sumeria, for example, it was survived by Ziusudra; in Babylonia, by Uta-napishtim (see page 81). In ancient Greece, the survivors Deucalion and his wife Pyrrha, wishing to repeople the world, were told by the goddess Themis to 'throw the bones of thy mother' behind them. These 'bones' were, of course, the stones and rocks of the earth, which was the body of the Great Mother Gaia. The stones that Deucalion threw became men, those that Pyrrha threw became women. In an Aztec flood myth, the survivors were a man, Coxcoxtli and a woman, Xochiquetzal, who, like Noah, sailed the waters in a boat and ended on a mountain called Colhuacan.

So Michabo called the musk-rat, and sent her off with the same instructions as before. How long she was gone no one can be sure – an hour or a day or a year or more – but what is sure is that this time, when the muskrat returned, she held between her teeth a tiny clod of earth, just big enough to allow the Master to do his work.

Michabo took the clod of earth and, with his magic powers of creation, made it into an island and sent it floating out on the water and the island grew and grew into a vast land with hills and valleys and plains. And there were trees on this new land but they were bare of branches, so Michabo loosed his arrows at the trunks, and they took root in the bark and became new branches and burgeoned with fresh green leaves, and the world that Michabo had made was more beautiful to behold than you can imagine.

As for the muskrat who had helped to bring about this great work of creation, Michabo rewarded her by making her his wife, and it is their children and their children's children and all the generations that followed who have been living ever since in the wonderful new world that Michabo made from a tiny clod of earth, long, long ago.

BELOW: MICHABO'S RAVEN WAS UNSUCCESSFUL IN FINDING EVEN THE TINIEST GRAIN OF SOIL. FOR SOME NORTHWESTERN TRIBES, HOWEVER, HE WAS A MAJOR GOD WHO CREATED THE WORLD.

old – but he needed help. He called the raven:

'Go out across the water,' he said, 'and bring me back one grain of soil so that I may make a new world from the remains of the old.' With a swish of wings and a croaking cry, the raven flew off to do the Master's bidding. But when it returned, it brought nothing.

So Michabo called the otter:

'Go out across the water,' he said again, 'and bring me back one grain of soil so that I may make a new world from the remains of the old.' With a flip of its sleek body, the otter dived into the water and was soon out of sight. But when it returned, it brought nothing.

In Indian mythology, there is not a single once-and-for-all creation and once-and-for-all destruction, but endlessly repeating cycles of creation and destruction. This famous myth describes how one of these creations was missing certain elements. Compare the sensual quality of this story with the starkness of the Norse creation myth on page 20. Compare, too, Odin's theft of the Mead of All–Knowing on page 92 with the deviousness showed by the gods here.

CHURNING THE OCEAN OF MILK

Throughout all the cycles of creation, throughout all the ages of time, the devas and asuras have been enemies. Throughout all the cycles of creation, throughout all the ages of time, those same gods and demons have needed offerings of amrita, the butter of immortality, to ensure their continued power.

Now it so happened, at the beginning of the second cycle of creation, that the new universe that arose was incomplete, for from it were missing fourteen precious things, among which was the amrita. Anxious that without the sacred butter they would lose their supremacy,

the gods conferred as to what they should do. There was only one solution: they would have to churn the great ocean of milk until they brought out of it all the precious things that were missing.

The gods knew, however, that they could not accomplish this task unaided, so they asked the demons to help them in churning the milky ocean, promising them a share of the amrita in return. Enticed by this thought, the demons agreed. But a fish is soon caught that nibbles at the first bait, and if the demons had not been so greedy they would have realized that the gods had no intention of sharing anything with them.

And so the great work began. For a churning stick the gods and the demons uprooted Mount Mandara, and wound around it Vâsuki, King of the Serpents, to use as a rope to rotate the mountain. Then, with the demons at his head and the gods at his tail, the assembled company began to

haul on Vâsuki, pulling first one way and then the other, until slowly, with much creaking and groaning, the huge mountain began to revolve.

As the gods and demons pulled harder and harder the mountain began to turn faster and faster. And so great was the heat from its spinning that it set the mountain slopes alight, and the fire would have consumed every plant, every animal, every bird there, had not Indra, Lord of the Rain and the Storm, sent a rainstorm to quench the blaze.

And so great was the weight of the mountain that it would have broken through the earth itself, had not Vishnu the Preserver assumed the form of Kurma the turtle and borne on his back the weight of the mountain. And Vishnu was both the turtle beneath the mountain and the god sitting in glory on top.

And so great was the labour of Vâsuki King of the Serpents that a torrent of venom began to pour from his jaws that would have killed gods, demons and all living things, had not Shiva the Destroyer drunk the poison and so saved the world. But as Shiva swallowed the poison, a little of it burnt his throat leaving a blue mark, which is why he is called Nilakantha, which means 'blue throat'.

And at the end of a thousand years of churning, the gods and demons were at last rewarded, for the precious missing things began to appear out of the ocean of milk. First came the great cow Surabhi, wetnurse of everything living, and then other treasures followed – Varunî, Goddess of Wine; Parijata the Tree of Paradise whose scented flowers perfumed all

SEA GIFTS
The image of the primordial ocean delivering up its treasures alludes – as does the Magical Cauldron, the Fountain of Youth, and even the baptismal font – to the cosmic womb of the Great Mother, the 'fons et origo', the Source of All Things. The key property these motifs all share is, quite simply, the gift of life, both physically and spiritually. In the Bible, for example, Jonah is swallowed and then disgorged by a great fish that symbolizes the sea, in a ritual of death and rebirth, while the act of baptism confers spiritual birth. In Irish myth, the Dagda, the 'Good God', sustained life with his inexhaustible Cauldron of Plenty, from which none ever went unsatisfied.

the world; the Apsuras, Nymphs of Grace and Beauty. Out of the milky sea, too, rose the sun and Soma, God of the Moon and of Amrita. And there also, floating on the creamy waves, seated in a lotus blossom and crowned with flowers, was Lakshmi, radiant Goddess of Fortune and Plenty, and consort to Vishnu.

Finally came the treasure that all the gods and demons had been waiting for – the amrita itself, contained in a cup held by the physician god Dhanvantari. As soon as the demons saw him, they lunged at him and would have made away with the amrita, had Vishnu not assumed yet another form, this time that of a voluptuous woman named Mohini. Seduced by her beauty and filled with desire for her, the demons agreed to allow her to share out the amrita. But no sooner had the gods received their portion than Mohini mysteriously vanished, with the faintest echo of a tinkling laugh, leaving the demons empty-handed.

And that is how the gods kept the amrita for themselves, and how they continued to reign supreme over all of creation.

LEFT: PULLING ON VÂSUKI, THE GODS AND DEMONS ENGAGE IN THE GARGANTUAN TASK OF CHURNING UP THE OCEAN.

THE DEATH OF BALDER THE BEAUTIFUL

The Balder in this famous Norse tale is a god of the light, a kind of sun god, a northern Apollo. The mistletoe that is used to kill him is a plant traditionally plucked at midsummer in Scandinavia, so there may be underlying symbolic associations, too, of the sun being 'killed' at the summer solstice when it is at its zenith and before it begins its decline into winter.

ABOVE: A VIKING FORGE STONE SHOWING THE FACE OF THE GOD LOKI WITH HIS LIPS SEWN TOGETHER IN PUNISHMENT FOR ONE OF HIS MANY MISDEMEANOURS. IT WAS LOKI WHO ENGINEERED THE DEATH OF BALDER.

Balder was fine and Balder was fair and Balder was shining as the sun and he was loved by men and by gods, with his snow-bright brow and corn-gold locks. He was the son of Allfather Odin and his wife Frigg, and his days were spent in harmony and happiness in Asgard, the home of the gods that lies in the upper world of heaven.

But a time came when Balder's sleep was troubled by dark dreams filled with gloomy shadows and monstrous forms, and when he awoke his heart was heavy with foreboding and he could no longer smile.

Noticing his sadness, his father and mother questioned him as to the source of his sorrow, and Balder told them of his dreams. And when Odin heard what Balder said, he determined to go himself to Niflheim, the Land of the Dead, to discover the meaning of the visions that so disturbed his son's mind.

And so it was that Odin, the one-eyed magician god, sitting astride Sleipnir, his eight-legged horse, rode out of Asgard, down the Trembling Roadway – the rainbow bridge of Bifröst – to Midgard, the home of men, and from there along the long and lonely road of no return, that no living soul could tread, to Niflheim, region of mists and ice and gloom that is home to the dead. Here he entered the hall of Hel, Queen of the Dead, and saw a great banquet prepared, and all the dead sitting at table bedecked in gold and jewels and silks, and plates of gold and silver on the table, and every bench and chair filled except for one, kept vacant for some absent guest of honour yet to come.

Without being observed, Odin silently passed by the throng and arrived at the grave of a seeress whose ghost he raised by the power of his magic.

'Who is this who troubles my sleep, and will not let me rest?' the spectre demanded, and when Odin – disguising his true identity – asked about the meaning of Balder's dreams, and in whose honour the deathly banquet was laid, the seeress replied:

'Hel waits to welcome the shining Balder, the Beautiful One, to her table and keeps for him a chair, and the halls of the dead will resound with rejoicing at his arrival …'

She further told Odin that it would be at the hand of blind Höd, Balder's own brother, that he would die, from a wound caused by a fatal weapon unknowingly and innocently hurled. And with that, she vanished back into the grave and the earth covered her as before, still and silent and cold.

FRIGG TRIES TO OUTWIT FATE

When Odin heard the terrible prophesy of the seeress, he rode as fast as Sleipnir would carry him, and that was fast indeed, back along the lonely road from Niflheim, back into Midgard the home of men, back over Bifröst and into Asgard. There Frigg and the entire company of gods were waiting anxiously for his arrival, and for such news as he might bring. Clamouring around him, they were filled with despair when they heard what he had discovered, that Balder was going to die.

But Frigg refused to give up hope. In defiance of destiny, she declared that she would travel through all the nine worlds of creation and would elicit a promise from every living thing, and every thing that was not living, that it would not harm Balder.

And that is exactly what she did, and wherever she made her tearful plea a promise was given. The people of Midgard promised, the

BELOW: AN 8TH-CENTURY VIKING FUNERARY STONE, FROM GOTLAND IN SWEDEN, SHOWING ODIN ASTRIDE HIS EIGHT-LEGGED HORSE SLEIPNIR, BEING WELCOMED BY A VALKYRIE, A NORSE WARRIOR-MAIDEN, TO VALHALLA.

dwarves and the giants promised, the animals and birds and insects promised, the trees promised, fire, water and metal promised, even the rocks and stones of the mountains and the pebbles of the shore promised, for everyone and every thing in all the world loved Balder.

THE GODS PLAY A DANGEROUS GAME

Then the gods, to amuse themselves, decided to make a game of Balder's invincibility and, with the Shining One in the centre of a circle of players, began to hurl at him all manner of weapons, while he, protected by the magic of the promises, remained unharmed. Much merriment and laughter was heard in Gladsheim, the hall of the gods, as sticks and stones and burning brands bounced off Balder as if deflected by some invisible power, and the commotion thus caused attracted the curiosity of Loki, shape-shifter and mischief-maker.

Now Loki had always held himself apart from the other gods, and in his evil heart the flower of hatred and envy flourished. Where others wished well, he wished ill; where others wished for harmony he sought to sow discord; and he was the only one out of all the gods that hated Balder and all his radiant beauty and goodness.

So, taking on the shape of an aged crone, crooked and bent double over a stick, Loki approached Frigg and asked her the purpose of the gods' game. The unsuspecting Frigg explained the whole story; she told him of Balder's dream; she told him of Odin's journey to Niflheim to discover the meaning of the omens that had troubled Balder's sleep; and she told him how she herself had travelled the nine worlds to elicit promises from every living thing and every thing not living that it would not harm her beloved son.

'Every thing?' asked the crone. 'Was there not one thing, one single thing, in the whole of creation, that thou hast overlooked?'

And the goddess admitted that, yes, there was one thing, and that was a little plant that grew on the oak by the entrance to Valhalla, the hall of dead heroes. She had not asked for its promise for she considered it too insignificant to be able to do any harm.

That plant was the mistletoe.

This was just the knowledge that Loki sought, and armed with it he located the mistletoe, plucked it, and returned to the gods, still at their sport. And there, by the side of the happy company, sat Höd, who was unable to join in the entertainment because he could not see. Loki crept up behind him.

'Let not unseeing eyes keep thee from the game,' he cooed, 'come, let me guide thy hand,' and he placed in the blind god's fingers the mistletoe dart, raised the god's hand and let fly, and no sooner had the mistletoe left Höd's grasp than it pierced Balder's heart and he fell down dead.

And when no cheer or laughter greeted Höd's ears, only silence, and when he realized that he had been tricked into killing his beloved brother, he cried out in agony, and the gods would have punished Loki then and there but they could not for they stood in Gladsheim and it was hallowed ground.

What a wailing and a weeping then rang out through all of Asgard. As the news spread of the god's death, every living thing shed tears of sorrow that fell as thickly as the rains that fall in winter.

BALDER SAILS BEYOND THE SUNSET

The gods gave Balder such a funeral as is fit for only the greatest of heroes. They placed his body on his ship, Ringhorn, and so heavy was it that they had to summon the mighty giantess Hyrrokin to heave it into the water. Seeing his lifeless body thus, Balder's wife Nanna felt her heart break and she died, too. Her body was placed next to that of her husband, along with the body of his faithful horse.

A pyre was built on the ship, and gifts of precious things and useful objects such as one has in life and needs in the life hereafter were arranged on the deck. Then Odin stepped on board and placed on the arm of his dead son his gold armband Draupnir, the magic ring that on every ninth night dropped eight rings of equal value. And when he had done this, the Allfather bent down and placed his lips by his son's ear and whispered into it secret words, and to this day no one knows what it is that Odin said to Balder.

The pyre was ignited, the thunder god Thor raised his hammer and intoned the sacred words of blessing, and then – watched by a vast assembly of gods and giants and dwarves

THE GODS TRY TO BRING BALDER BACK FROM THE DEAD

While his body was thus burning, Balder's spirit had travelled to Niflheim, the Land of the Dead, where Hel had been awaiting him all this time. And the gods, in the hope that they might persuade the Queen of the Underworld to release her newest incumbent, sent a messenger by the name of Hermod to her, to plead their case. Nine days and nine nights it took Hermod to reach the icy-cold realm of Hel, and when he entered her hall he saw there, sitting in the high seat of honour, Balder the Beautiful, with his wife Nanna beside him.

The goddess received Hermod with

and elves – the great vessel Ringhorn bearing for the last time the body of her master and garlanded and crowned with the flames of glory, glided out to sea.

And as the ship slowly sank behind the horizon, behind the backbone of the sea, the blood-red setting sun melted into the fiery waves and darkness descended like the cloak of death over all of heaven and earth.

courtesy, heard his case, and agreed to release Balder – but on one condition: that every living thing and every thing not living in heaven and on earth must wish for his return, and as a sign they must all weep for Balder.

And before Hermod left the hall of Hel, the ghost of Balder approached him and took Draupnir, Odin's golden armband, off his arm and handed it to Hermod, saying, 'Take this ring to my father. Give it to him in remembrance of me.'

And Hermod, fighting back his tears, left gloomy Nifleim and made the long journey back to Asgard.

THE WORLD WEEPS FOR BALDER

The gods immediately set about the task of doing what was required to ensure Balder's return. Accordingly, they sent messengers far and wide, to all the nine worlds, and asked that all might weep for Balder, so that the power of their tear flood might raise him from the dead. And all that were asked agreed – people, animals, wood, stone, metal, fire, water, all of these wept for Balder, and the sound of their crying was like the howling of a great storm when wild winds bend the trees and curtains of rain cascade from the clouds.

There was one, however, the last to be approached, who refused to weep. This was an old giantess by the name of Thökk whom the gods' messengers came upon in a cavern high in the mountains.

'Weep for Balder? Why should I weep for Balder?' she said. 'Never in all my days did he do anything for me. No, let him stay where he is – let Hel keep what is hers!'

And so it was, because there was one living thing that would not shed tears, that the gods could not meet Hel's condition, and Balder was fated to remain in Niflheim for ever. And who was this giantess who alone had caused this sad end? None other than Loki himself, of course, the shape-shifter and evil-doer.

As a punishment for his treachery, the gods banished Loki from Asgard, and bound him in chains in a deep cave, and there he languishes still. But one day … one day he will break free of his fetters and will rouse a great host of giants and other monsters and the host will converge on Vigrid, the Plain of Heaven, to do battle with the gods … and that day will signal the beginning of the end, for it will be Ragnarok, when gods and men and all that inhabit the nine worlds are destroyed in an apocalypse of flame and flood.

And when that dread day will come, whether soon or late, not even the wisest among us can say …

In Norse mythology, the ending of the world (triggered by the killing of the sun god Balder: see pages 38–43) is known as Ragnarok, the 'Destruction of the Powers' – surely one of the most terrifying visions of the apocalypse ever dreamed of in the wildest nightmares of mankind. There is, however, always hope, for in our end is our beginning …

RAGNAROK

With fire and water the world began, and with fire and water it will end.

On the day that Loki escapes his chains – Loki whose evil schemes brought about the death of Balder the Beautiful and who was imprisoned by the gods in punishment – on that day black omens and forbidding portents will be seen in Asgard, home of the gods, and Midgard, home of men, as the rumbling clouds of Ragnarok gather.

Fimbulvetr, the Great Winter, will descend on Midgard and it will continue for three years without abating, bringing with it snow and ice and endless night. Warring and evil deeds and unnatural acts will fill the lives of men – father will kill son; brother will slay brother; mother will lie with son; brother will bed sister.

Out of the iron wood Skoll will come, the wolf whose desire it has been, since the begin-

TOP: A CARVED WOODEN PANEL FROM ICELAND SHOWING ODIN BEING SWALLOWED BY THE WOLF FENRIR. LEFT: ANOTHER DEPICTION OF THE SAME EVENT, SHOWN HERE ON THE PANEL OF A CROSS FROM THE ISLE OF MAN.

ning of time, to devour the sun. At Ragnarok, it will achieve its end. First the sun's rays will disappear and then the sun itself, like a great yolk turned blood-red, will slide into the wolf's hungry maw. The moon will suffer a similar fate, eaten by Skoll's wolf brother, Hati.

In all the nine worlds the call to arms will go up. Three cocks will crow – red Fjalar will alert the giants; another, rust-red, will rouse the dead; Gullinkambi the Golden Comb will wake the warriors of Valhalla who sleep the sleep of death – and at the same time Heimdall, the watchman of heaven, will raise his horn Gjall and blow on it a blast loud enough to be heard through all the worlds.

With a roll of thunder that will shake the nine worlds and a flash of lightning that will crack the sky in two like a shattered dome of glass, the fire giants will come from Muspell the Land of Fire, led by Surt with his flaming sword. From the west will come the phantom ship Naglfar, made of dead men's nails, captained by Hrym and filled with his fellow giants. And out of the freezing mists of Niflheim, home of the dead, another great hulk will emerge, manned by a grey and ghostly crew. At the helm will be Loki himself, and there, too, will be Fenrir the wolf, whose open jaws stretch from earth to heaven. And the ships of death will pitch about on the great swell of waves lashed by the writhing and twisting of the world serpent Jormungand.

As this terrible host storms towards the field of war across Bifröst the Rainbow Bridge that joins Midgard to Asgard, the rainbow will collapse and burst into flame. Then, on Vigrid the Plain of Heaven, that stretches one hundred and twenty leagues in every direction, the gods and their foes will join in a battle of the most savage butchery, at the end of which all the gods will be dead, and the world will begin to disintegrate. The stars – like birds too tired to fly – will drop from the sky; the earth, set alight by the fire giant Surt, will be swallowed in flames. And in the end, the all-consuming ocean will rise and submerge all in the silent deep-sea of oblivion.

That is how the world will end …

… and this is how it will begin.

Slowly, from out of the belly of the deep, a new earth will be delivered, with mountains and valleys and rivers, with singing birds, grazing animals, and fields of corn sown by no known hand. In this brave new world a new race of gods will arise, among whom will be two old faces – those of Balder and Höd. There will be mortals, too, ready to repeople the world. For while the apocalypse rages one man and one woman, whose names are Lif and Lifthrasir, will take shelter in Hoddmimir's Wood which is none other than Yggdrasil, the tree that frames the world. Here, in the heart of the wood, they will survive while all else perishes, sustained on the dew of the morning, which is the water of life.

BELOW: THIS SILVER VIKING PENDANT FROM SWEDEN IS THOUGHT TO REPRESENT BALDER ON HIS HORSE. IT WAS BALDER'S MURDER THAT EVENTUALLY LEAD TO RAGNAROK.

ELEMENTS &
CELESTIAL BODIES

Even in the modern scientific world, we can still experience some of the awe that earlier peoples must have felt for the forces of nature and for the phenomena of the natural world. The stories in this chapter are suffused with that wonder and sense of awe at forces far greater than man.

CHAPTER TWO

Australian aboriginals told this story to explain the waxing and waning of the moon. Unlike the Indo-European tradition in which the moon is decidedly female, here the moon is male.

THE DISAPPEARING MOON

When frogs could speak and fish had feet and monkeys chewed tobacco, when camels drank wine and danced with swine and hens sang quack, quack, quacko ... then, in those far-off days, the Moon came down from the sky and walked abroad, as do you and I.

Now the Moon was a curious-looking fellow, as round as a barrel, with tiny arms and legs as thin as chicken bones, and two bright and shining eyes. In spite of his strange appearance, he was on the whole a happy-go-lucky sort and during his wanderings enjoyed whistling and singing to himself, for he had a fine, clear tenor voice. But sometimes, just sometimes, he would feel sad for he had no companion with whom to spend his days, and he decided that he should find himself a wife.

And so he journeyed from village to village, where he would single out the prettiest girls and try to win their affections. But the girls could not take him seriously as a suitor, and secretly joked about his appearance and giggled at his clumsy ways for he was not practised in the arts of love.

Soon everyone in all the villages knew of the Moon's purpose, and anyone who saw him coming would call out: 'Watch out, the Moon is coming! Tell your daughters to hide!'

ABOVE: WATCHED BY A FULL MOON, A GROUP OF AUSTRALIAN ABORIGINES FISH BY TORCHLIGHT WHILE OTHERS COOK FISH OVER CAMP FIRES, FROM A SERIES OF DRAWINGS BY JOSEPH LYCETT (C.1775–1828).

Now it so happened, one clear, cloudless evening, when the sky was spattered and spangled with stars, that the Moon was strolling along the banks of a river, whistling and singing to himself as was his wont, for he was not one to stay down-hearted for long. And there, just a little further along the bank, two village girls – who did not know that the Moon was nearby – heard his beautiful singing wafting towards them through the balmy evening air.

'Surely someone with such a beautiful voice must have a beautiful face,' said they to each other, and at once began to weave dream-pictures in their minds of the voice's owner – a tall and handsome warrior, no doubt, with clear eyes and strong arms and a brave heart, the kind of man who would make a good husband for any girl.

Stifling their excitement, the girls hid in some bushes and waited for their dream's vision to appear – but what was their surprise when, instead of the handsome young warrior they were expecting, along came the funniest-looking man they had ever seen, with a body as round as a barrel and tiny arms and legs as thin as chicken bones.

Laughing, they dashed from the bushes to their canoe, leapt into it and began to paddle across the river.

'Wait!' called the Moon. 'I am hungry and tired. Have pity on me … take me with you.'

At this the girls relented for they were not unkind. They came back and told the Moon that he might use their canoe to cross the river, but he would have to row it himself. When the Moon told them he did not know how to row, they agreed to tow the canoe across the water themselves. And so, with the Moon in the canoe and the girls waist-high in the water, they began to pull him across.

But when they were only a quarter of the way over, the Moon became playful and started tickling the girls under the arms and trying to kiss them. Not once but twice did they tell him to desist, but when he still paid no heed, they hesitated no further but just tossed him, barrel-body, bony limbs and all, into the water. They watched as he sank, seeing first his whole sad, shining face looking up at them, then only half, then only a sliver, then nothing. The Moon had disappeared completely.

The story of what had happened to the Moon spread to all the villages, and the crow, who understands all things, told the people how it would be from then on, and everything happened as he said.

From that day on, the Moon was like one who is ashamed to be seen. First he would peep out of his home in the land where the spirits live. Then, as the days passed and he became a little bolder, he would venture forth more and more until the whole glory of his face was revealed.

But the Moon, like man, never learns, for each time he turned his shining face on some girl and smiled at her his shining smile but failed to win her heart, he would slowly turn his face from the world again, fading bit by bit until all that was visible was a crescent-shaped slice of silver … and then that, too, would vanish from view.

And that is why, from that day to this, the Moon continues to hide his face – and if this tale is true only those can say who were there to see, which is neither you nor I.

THE SEASONAL MOON

The endlessly repeating phases of the moon gave people a model for understanding the mysteries of birth, life and death. It also gave them hope. If the moon was, as the Babylonians said, the 'fruit that grows from itself', if a new moon could be born out of the death of the old, then life, too, could be relied upon to renew itself. The lunar pattern parallels the seasons, spring being the burgeoning moon, summer the fulsome moon, autumn the ageing moon. There is a fourth lunar phase, too, known as the dark moon – three days at the end of the cycle when the moon disappears – which parallels winter, that period of hidden gestation when all signs of life have gone. Interestingly, three days was the span of time spent by Jonah in the belly of the whale and Christ in the tomb before their respective 'rebirths'.

This Aztec myth tells how the sun avenged the murder of his mother, and in so doing created the day. The battle between the sun and his siblings was commemorated and re-enacted by priests at the temple of Tenochtitlan, in a ritual involving human sacrifice. Huitzilopochtli, who appears here as the Sun God, is an aspect of the god Tezcatlipoca.

HOW NIGHT TURNED INTO DAY

Long, long ago, before the Sun was born, there was only endless night, lit by the Moon, Coyolxauhqui, and her four hundred brothers, the Stars, whose name was Centzon-Huitznahuas, which means 'the four hundred southerners'. The Moon and the Stars were the children of Coatlicue, the Mother Goddess.

Now one day – or rather night – Coatlicue, dressed as usual in her skirt of serpents, was sweeping out her house at Tula, the serpent mountain, when she looked up into the starry sky and saw a mysterious object floating gently towards her from above. As it got closer, she recognized it as a circle of feathers, which came to rest on her bosom. She was intrigued as to where this unwished-for gift might have come from, but soon put such questions out of her mind, for what she had received was, after all, no more than a ball of fluff. It was not long, however, before the significance of this incident became clear, for just a few days after being touched by the feathers from heaven, Coatlicue discovered that she was pregnant …

When her daughter Coyolxauhqui the Moon heard the news, she was shocked and angry. She knew that the child her mother carried was not the child of Mixcoatl, husband to Coatlicue. Who, then, was the infant's

THE CONQUERING HERO

The avenging Huitzilopochtli is reminiscent of the Indo-European solar hero, the conquering sun who with his rays banishes the evils of darkness. From around 4500 BC, warlike Aryan invaders swept south and west in progressive waves from their homelands in the steppes between the Black and Caspian Seas, and they brought with them a new image of divinity – a male, warrior sky god who would not share power but insisted instead on being absolute head of the household, maintaining his position with weapons such as the sword of lightning and the bolt of thunder.

MITHRA

The conquering sun is an extension of this archetype, and one good example is the Persian god Mithra, whose worship was widespread right across Europe and whose birthday was celebrated in Rome just after the winter solstice, the turning point of the year when the days begin to lengthen, and when 'the sun prepares to make the day longer than the night'. His annual rebirth – the victory of light over darkness – was celebrated on 'Dies Natalis Solis Invictus', meaning 'the Birthday of the Unconquered Sun'. This fell on 25 December, which was later adopted as Christmas Day and is still celebrated today.

ABOVE: COATLICUE, THE 'LADY OF THE SERPENT SKIRT'. LIKE HINDU KALI, SHE WAS THE MOTHER OF LIFE AND DEATH, AND LIKED TO WEAR A NECKLACE OF SKULLS.

father? How could her mother dishonour herself and all of her family in this way? And the enraged Coyolxauhqui stormed off to her four hundred brothers, and demanded that they kill their mother, that they cut off her head, to punish her for this terrible thing she had done.

Persuaded by their sister, the Stars raised their weapons and sliced their mother's head from her neck, whereupon the child she had been carrying sprang fully formed from her body, and he was an awesome sight to behold. His body was coloured blue, and the feathers of humming-birds adorned his head and his left leg, and in his left hand he carried a fire serpent. He was Huitzilopochtli, 'the left-handed humming-bird', God of the Sun. And Huitzilopochtli fell on his brothers and sister, and then what a battle there was! But in the end the Sun was victorious, and the Stars and the Moon lay dead at his feet.

In this way, the Sun turned the night into day, as he has done every day since when he comes over the eastern horizon, shooting his arrows of light into the night sky and banishing the darkness.

Quetzalcoatl, the main character in this myth, was originally the chief god of the Toltecs of central Mexico and was later adopted by the Aztecs, who conquered them. Tezcatlipoca was his great enemy. One of the alternative endings to the story led to a tragic misunderstanding, for when the Aztecs, under the emperor Montezuma, saw the galleons of the conquistadores, they believed them to be the party of the returning Quetzalcoatl and treated them as gods.

THE EVENING STAR

There were once four brothers, whose names were Tezcatlipoca, Huitzilopochtli, Xipe Totec, and Quetzalcoatl. The first was the black Sorceror God, possessor of the smoking mirror, and he lived in the north; the second was the blue God of War and and he lived in the south; the third was the red God of the Corn, who each year allowed himself to be flayed like the maize seed that loses its skin when it sprouts, and he lived in the east; and the fourth was the blue, feathered-serpent God of the Wind, Lord of the Calendar and Zodiac, and he lived in the west.

Now these four brothers could not agree and were always quarrelling over who should rule in each of the five suns, the five ages of time. Tezcatlipoca had ruled the first sun, the age of earth, and Quetzalcoatl the second, that of wind, and it was the schemes and intrigues of the former that would bring about the downfall of the latter.

ABOVE: THE TURQUOISE AND SHELL-ENCRUSTED MASK OF QUETZALCOATL, FORMED FROM ENTWINING SNAKES.

A master of deception and trickery, Tezcatlipoca was not one to be trusted. By means of his magic he could assume many shapes. Sometimes he was a fleeting shadow, glimpsed out of the corner of the eye; sometimes he was the jaguar that slinks through the night; sometimes he was a giant that roamed after sunset, wrapped in an ashen veil and carrying his head in his hand. And whenever any of the people saw these things, they knew that they had seen Tezcatlipoca.

With evil in his heart, the treacherous Tezcatlipoca conceived a plan to destroy his brother, the gentle Quetzcoatl. Soothing him with wine and ensorcelling him with magic, he coaxed Quetzcoatl into lying with his own sister Quetzalpetlatl – or perhaps it was not his sister but another, a demon goddess who, under the magician god's touch, had assumed a false appearance.

Whatever the case may be, it is true to say that when Quetzalcoatl was returned to his senses, he was so ashamed of what he had done that he determined to leave the world for ever. He built a funeral pyre, placed himself upon it, set it alight, and burnt to death in the flames. And when the little birds saw the god's remains lying there, they flew down and lifted out his heart and placed it in the sky, and you may see it there still, for it is the planet Venus, also known as the Evening Star.

Or perhaps the god did not place himself on a pyre, for there is another ending to this sad tale, and it tells how the god buried his treasure, set light to his palace of silver and shells and, accompanied by his attendants now transformed into brightly coloured birds, sailed off on a raft of serpents toward the east, promising to return one day.

And the people waited and waited, gazing out over the eastern sea for signs of a ship bearing their lost god. Some of them died and some of them lived, and when they grew old they passed the story on to their children, of how the god would one day return, and the word was passed on from one generation to the next and that is why, when galleons appeared from the east, the people believed that Quetzalcoatl had at last come back to them, and they gave the strangers on board such gifts as are fitting for a god, including Quetzalcoatl's turquoise mask and also his feathered cloak. But the strangers were not gods, merely men greedy for gold and riches, and they imposed their rule on the people and made them slaves of an alien race.

But perhaps one day Quetzalcoatl will truly return, on his raft of serpents attended by flights of rainbow birds. Or perhaps he is with us now, up there in the twilight sky – Quetzalcoatl the Evening Star, heralding the coming of night.

BELOW: THIS MIXTEC PAINTING SHOWS TEZCATLIPOCA LURING THE EARTH MONSTER FROM THE WATERS USING HIS FOOT AS BAIT.

In this exquisite Maori myth, the origin of the rainbow is explained. The quality of the imagery is very reminiscent of that found in Native American myths, for both show a profound sensitivity to the natural world and an almost unbearable poignancy of narrative.

THE MIST AND THE RAINBOW

Once upon a time, long, long ago, among the shadowy peaks of the high, green mountains, so high that their heads are clothed in cloud, there lived a race of spirits, the fairy spirits of the sky. One day, two of them decided to visit earth. Their names were Hine-pukohu-rangi and Hine-wai – Sky Mist Woman and Water Woman – and they were sisters, one the soft mist that drifts on cloudy days and the other the gentle rain that accompanies it.

Now as anyone who has ever had dealings with the fairy folk knows, fairy women are dazzlingly beautiful, and in this they outshine mortal women as the shimmering moon outshines the numberless stars. And so, when Sky Mist Woman entered the dwelling of Uenuku, a mortal man, one evening as the dusk was falling, Uenuku was entranced by her beauty and fell deeply in love with her. He begged her to become his wife and she consented, but she would only come to him when the fire had gone out, in the night which is the magic time when fairies are abroad. There was another condition, too: he must never, ever, tell anyone about her, at least not until they had a child.

'For if you do,' she said, 'I will fly back to the sky and you will never see me again.' This is the way of the fairy people.

All worked well for a time. Every night Sky Mist Woman would come to Uenuku, and every morning, just as the dawn was lightening the sky and turning it the pearly grey of a dove's wing, her sister Water Woman would call to her, telling her that it was time to go, and the two sisters would return together to the sky, and when Uenuku woke he would be alone once more.

Now for a while Uenuku was happy with this arrangement, but as the days passed and the months passed, he wanted more and more to tell someone his secret, that he had a fairy

FAIRY WAYS

Although they are the product of cultures at the opposite ends of the world, the supernatural women in this story recall the fairies of Celtic lore. Many a Celtic fairy story features an otherwordly wife who stays with her earthly husband only on condition that he does not do something, and if he disobeys her prohibition – which, of course, he always does – she will leave him. Celtic and Maori fairy-women also share the same nocturnal visiting habits, as do many other supernatural beings (see, for example, 'Cupid and Psyche' on page 162).

wife who was more beautiful than any woman on earth. Mindful of his wife's warning, however, at first he only told his secret to the walls of his house; but the walls said nothing, so he told his secret to the birds in the wood; but the birds said nothing, so he entrusted his secret to human ears, telling it to one of the other men of the village. And that was his undoing. Oh, how quickly the news then spread to all the people of the village, like a fire running through the forest, until it was a secret no more: 'Uenuku has a fairy wife!'

At once, everyone came rushing and running and bustling and busying, to tell Uenuku what he should do.

'Do not let her escape! Hold her fast as she tries to fly away,' advised one.

'Stay awake all night so that you can see when she tries to leave,' recommended another.

But a third villager, more cunning than the rest and who thought himself versed in the ways of fairies, said.

'Do none of these things. Stop up all the chinks and cracks of your house so that no light can enter, and then your wife will think that the day has not come and she will stay with you.'

And that is exactly what Uenuku did, and the inside of his house became as dark as the inside of a cave.

That night Sky Mist Woman came to him again, but when the dawn lightened the sky once more and her sister called to her to go, she replied:

'It is not time to go yet. It is still night – can you not see how dark the house is?' And she

darkness, only to be fixed in their present locations when touched by the light of day. Others were believed to be early ancestors of the Maoris, similarly transmuted by the rays of the rising sun. According to legend, these peaks and ranges, numbering more than 150 in South Island, were the petrified former crew and passengers of the Araiteuru, the boat that had sailed south from Hawaiki, the Maori name for the mythic Savai'i, the ancestral Polynesian homeland of memory. Coming ashore at night and spreading out across the island, their metamorphosis took place with the sunrise, and there they still stand to this day, giant stone monuments to Maori history.

PUKETAPU

This conically shaped hill at Waihemo (Palmerston) had once been a woman called Puke-tapu. Having struggled ashore with the rest of the passengers of the Araiteuru, she had set off to look for firewood, for the night was cold. Returning with her bundle from the mouth of the Clutha River, the only place where wood could be found, she was overtaken by the sunrise and turned to stone where she stood. Some of the sticks from her bundle fell and metamorphosed into forests.

AORAKI

Known in English as Mount Cook, the highest peak in New Zealand's Southern Alps, Aoraki is said formerly to have been a small boy from the Araiteuru who was being carried on the shoulders of one of his relatives – which explains why he was taller than the others – when daylight struck him and turned him to stone.

KAITANGATA

Kai-tangata, who had also sailed on the Araiteuru, had brought painting materials with him. When the rays of the rising sun turned him to stone, he became a hill containing deposits of red ochre near the town of the same name.

REEFS AND ROCKS

The metamorphosis that overcame the passengers of the Araiteuru affected the vessel too. Swept by a gale as far as Shag Point – Matakaea – near Palmerston, she was transformed, along with Hipo, her captain, into a reef. Her cargo, washed ashore at Moeraki, was turned into boulders, and even the four great waves that swept her to her destruction solidified into rock, the crests and troughs of their rolling surge freezing in mid-movement to become the mountain ranges known as Horse Range, Old Man Range, Raggedy Range and Rough Range.

MAGIC MOUNTAINS

It is no mere narrative conceit that the spirit women in this Maori myth originate in the mountains. For the Maoris, aboriginal peoples who had sailed southward from other Polynesian islands further north and begun to settle in New Zealand from AD 1000, mountains had a great mystical presence. 'Tapu' mountains had sacred, forbidden summits, and peoples in different regions each had 'their own' magic mountain, its sacred peak expressing their collective 'mana' – psychic power or essence – and serving as a conduit between the earthly world and the divine realm of the sky. The thunder and lightning that cracked and flashed around such mountaintops were signs and omens of things to come, and caves here provided resting places for individuals of high rank among people to whom these peaks 'belonged'.

MOVING MOUNTAINS

Like the Cyanean Rocks or Symplegades of Greek myth that stood at the junction between the Bosphorus and Black Sea and moved together to crush any ship, including Jason's, that attempted to sail between them, the mountains of New Zealand have not always been stationary mounds of rock. Once, it was said, some had moved about under cover of lay down and went back to sleep, and her sister Water Woman returned to the sky alone.

And in the morning, when the sun was high, the people came and opened the door of the house and the bright light of day flooded into all the nooks and corners and crannies of the room and woke Uenuku and his wife. And when Sky Mist Woman saw that she had been tricked, she said nothing but quietly went to stand beneath the hole through which the smoke rises in the roof, and she raised her beautiful voice in song and sang a lament, a song of farewell, and the sound of it would have filled your eyes with tears and sent a shiver through the marrow of your bones for it was the sound of a mother keening for her child, the sound of a woman calling for her lost love, the sound of the desolate wind that haunts all the forlorn and lonely places of the world, a song of such sorrow as would break your heart.

And as she sang her song all her solid substance seemed to dissolve and she slowly floated up and out through the roof, her form and her voice fading from sight and hearing like a column of blue smoke melting into the air … and then she was gone. And among all those gathered there, not a sound was uttered, not a word was said, for all were silenced at the foolishness of what they had done.

And Uenuku searched through all the wide, wide world for his fairy wife until his hair was white and his body bent and buckled, but he never found her, and in the end death claimed him and in death he was transformed for he became the rainbow that comes with the mist. And in this form he was re-united with his beloved and to this day they are together and inseparable, for whenever you see Hine-puko-hu-rangi the soft Sky Mist, there too, you will see Uenuku the Rainbow.

THE BRIDGE OF HEAVEN

In many mythological traditions all over the world, the rainbow was viewed as the bridge between heaven and earth. Once, in a dimly remembered golden age before universal man's exclusion from Paradise, the rainbow had been an open pathway to all mortals, but now it offered access to heaven only to the chosen few, such as mythical heroes or shamans who had their own magical or mystical methods of entry.

THE RAINBOW SERPENT

The initiation rite of Australian medicine men involved ascent to the sky by means of the rainbow, pictured as an enormous snake, the Rainbow Serpent. Similarly, the Maori hero Tawhaki and the Hawaiian hero Aukelenuiaiku both climbed the rainbow on their regular visits to the celestial realm.

BIFROST

In Norse myth, the rainbow was Bifröst, the bridge the gods used for their to-ings and fro-ings to earth.

IRIS

In Greek myth, Iris (from whom we get 'iridescence') was both the rainbow itself and the goddess in whose guardianship it was held.

THE GREAT RIDGEPOLE

In Chinese tradition, the rainbow represented the union between the male and female principles, or yin and yang. It was known as the 'tai ch'i' or Great Ultimate.

THE SWORD BRIDGE

Because the rainbow (or the tree or the vine, or whatever other connecting symbol was used) no longer offered a means of celestial entry to the majority, the parallel image of the sword bridge (or hair bridge) arose. This placed a suitably impossible challenge before those who wished for access to the 'realm beyond' – they had to walk along a pathway as sharp as a razor's edge, as narrow as a hair. Crossing a sword bridge was the trial that Launcelot endured to rescue Guinevere from the Castle of Death.

THE RAINBOW MOTHER

Being both a bridge uniting the worlds and having seven prismatic colours that seemed to embody the essence of all substances, the rainbow was also associated with creation itself. The Australian Rainbow Serpent Mother was said to have made the world and all its people. The Yoruban Rainbow Goddess Oya created the elements; in the New World, she became Olla in Cuba and Puerto Rico, Yansa in Brazil, Damballah in Haiti.

In this popular legend from Chinese mythology, the Heavenly Spinner – or Spinster – is the daughter of the August Personage of Jade, or Father-Heaven, the Creator God and one of the supreme trinity of the Chinese pantheon. The star which the Heavenly Spinner personifies is Alpha in the Lyre, while her husband represents Beta and Gamma in Aquila. The Heavenly River is, of course, the Milky Way.

THE COWHERD AND THE HEAVENLY SPINNER

Once upon a time, there lived a young cowherd, the son of a poor widower. Every day, the cowherd would take the neighbouring farmer's cattle out to graze, and every night he would return. It was a simple enough life, and the cowherd was not unhappy with his lot. But one day, his father became ill and called his son to him for he knew he was dying.

'My son,' he said, 'I have no possessions in the world but a little piece of land and my faithful ox. These I leave to you. Guard the ox well, for one day, perhaps, he may bring you good fortune.' And so saying, he died.

The cowherd was overcome with grief for now he was alone in the world. But he heeded his father's words, and cared for the ox as well as he might and fed and watered him, and as

the months and then the years passed, the cowherd grew into a handsome young man.

One day, when he had harnessed the ox to his small wooden plough and was working the plot his father had left him, turning the rich, black earth as he went, he was amazed to hear the ox open his mouth and speak.

'You have tended me well,' said the ox, 'and a favour done is a boon earned. Follow my instructions exactly, and you will have a wife more beautiful and wonderful than any woman on earth. This is what you must do …'

This clearly was no ordinary ox, but some magical spirit in disguise. The cowherd paid careful attention to what the magic ox had to say, and the very next day, he stationed himself by the river, concealing himself behind a clump of trees, and waited to see if all would happen as the ox had said, and sure enough it did.

He had hardly been at his station for more than a few moments when he heard the sound of tinkling laughter disturbing the stillness of the air like ripples on a pond, and a group of

---

Above: An ox was the cowherd's ally. This ox-shaped vessel was made in the Qian Long period (1736–1795).

young women came into view. They were all beautiful, but one in their midst surpassed all the others in perfection. Her skin was as white as snow, with the sheen of a pearl. Her cheeks were lightly flushed, like the pink of cherry blossom in spring. Her eyes were shaped like almonds, her nose was small and fine, her lips two rosebuds, her hair blue-black as the raven's wing … and the robes she wore were unlike anything the cowherd had ever seen before, for they seemed to have stolen all the colours of the sky and were soft and light as floating clouds, and appeared to have been sewn without any seams. This vision of beauty was, in fact, no ordinary mortal woman but a goddess, daughter of the August Personage of Jade. She was Chih-nii the Heavenly Spinner, who wove the robes of the gods, and who, for a little idle amusement, had come down to earth with her handmaidens to bathe in the river.

Chih-nii and her companions removed their clothes, laying them down on the bank, and stepped into the cool, clear water of the stream. As soon as they were a sufficient distance away, the cowherd crept out of his hiding place and stole the featherlight, rainbow gown of the Heavenly Spinner, and waited ...; and, sure enough, just as the magic ox had foretold, when she returned and could not find her clothes, she was unable to return to heaven with the others.

So Chih-nii stayed on earth and became the cowherd's wife, and in time she bore two children, a boy and a girl. And then, one day, she said to the cowherd, 'Dear husband, do you remember the heavenly robes I was wearing when first you saw me? I would so love to try them on once more, for it is a long time since I have worn anything so fine. Tell me, dearest, where do you keep them hidden?'

And the cowherd, suspecting nothing, showed her the hiding place where the heavenly robes had been secreted all these long years – and no sooner had she put them on than she vanished, in the time it takes to blink an eye. Oh, and how the cowherd wept for his lost wife, oh, and how the children cried for their lost mother! But the magic ox came to the cowherd and said, 'Do not weep. You have tended me well, and a favour done is a boon earned. I will help you to find your wife. This is what you must do …'

The cowherd did exactly as the magic ox told him. He placed each of his children in a basket suspended at either end of a long pole, and placed the pole across his shoulders. Then, grasping the ox's tail, he shut his eyes tight … and in the time it takes to turn a hair, he found himself in heaven.

There he requested an audience with the August Personage of Jade and, when he had told his story and the tale was found to be true, the August Personage decided to make him immortal, so he turned him into a star that lies to the west of the Heavenly River, while Chih-nii the Heavenly Spinner became a star to the east. And on the seventh day of every seven days, the August Personage decreed, the pair might meet each other.

But Chih-nii and the cowherd misunderstood, and thought that they could only come together on the seventh day of the seventh month, and so they have done ever since. And because there is no bridge by which to cross the Heavenly River, on that day all the magpies fly up to heaven carrying twigs with which to form a pathway over the stream on which husband and wife may walk. And on the morning of that day it always rains, and the people say that the raindrops are the tears of Chih-nii the Heavenly Spinner and her husband the cowherd, weeping for joy to see each other again.

BELOW: MAGPIES FLUTTER AROUND THE COWHERD ON THIS CHINESE PORCELAIN BOWL, DATING FROM 1821–1850.

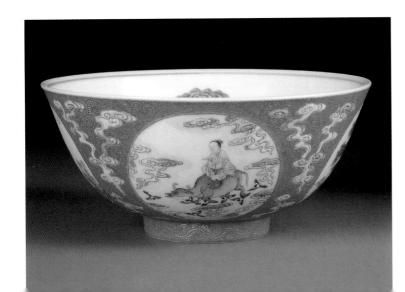

The hero of this Greek tale, Ulysses, is also known as Odysseus. The story of his long voyage home from the Trojan War was recounted in the epic poem, the 'Odyssey', by the Greek poet Homer. Aeolus, the other protagonist, was at first the Guardian of the Winds, but to Romans, he became the God of Wind. He gave his name to the Aeolian Harp, a device which emitted music when air moved over the strings.

ULYSSES AND THE BAG OF WINDS

Long, long ago, there was a king by the name of Aeolus, who lived on an island in the middle of the sea, far, far from land. Now this was no ordinary island like others, that are fixed in their place as a tree is rooted in the earth. This was a floating island, and it drifted serenely on the surface of the water like a galleon in full sail. Indeed, it was said that King Aeolus himself had invented the sail, for was he not

the King of the Winds? And was not his island the resting place of Boreas the North Wind, Zephyrus the West Wind, Eurus the East Wind, Notus the South Wind? And was it not Aeolus who alone could soothe or excite the winds and thus help or hinder sailors on the sea?

To this island one day came a ship bearing Ulysses, the King of Ithaca, and his crew, weary and battle-spent and on their way home from the war with Troy. Aeolus received Ulysses and his men with the greatest hospitality, inviting them to stay in his palace, where they rested and refreshed their strength, until they felt ready to continue their voyage.

As a parting gift, King Aeolus gave Ulysses a large bag – a wine-skin fastened with a silver cord in which he had enclosed all the winds but one – Zephyrus the West Wind, that would blow Ulysses' ship eastwards back home to Ithaca. As he handed over his gift, he warned Ulysses that the bag must on no account be opened until he and his men were safely home, or great misfortune would befall them.

Ulysses took the bag, thanked his host, and set off in his ship, with his men, towards the

wide blue horizon, and home. But his crew had seen Aeolus hand the wine-skin to their king, and they talked excitedly among themselves as to what it might hold. It was a gift from one king to another, so it must surely contain treasure – gold and jewels and other precious things, without doubt. They waited for the moment when they might seize it, untie the silver cord, and help themselves to whatever riches were concealed inside.

But Ulysses knew what his men had in mind, so he determined to steer the ship himself, and to go without sleep, until they had reached the shores of Ithaca. Day and night Ulysses stayed by the rudder, the bag guarded close by his side. With the coming of each morning, he watched Apollo as he rose in the east in his golden chariot and rode across the sky, driving before him the scudding clouds, Apollo's white cattle. With the coming of each evening, he gazed on Apollo's sister, shining Artemis, as she illuminated the starry sky and transformed the dark sea into molten silver. And all the while, Zephyrus was behind him, whispering in his ear and caressing the ship with his warm breath and puffing out the sails like the wings of a great bird, so that the vessel moved effortlessly over the smooth sea as the evening swan glides over the lake.

At last, Ulysses saw the peaks of Ithaca rising before him: he was nearly home. He could keep his eyes open no longer. He succumbed to sleep. And his men, impatient for the riches they believed the bag to hold, seized it, ripped off its silver cord, and unloosed its contents – and what a terrible storm then arose. The winds, confined for so long, sprang from captivity in all their power, and hit the ship from every direction at once. The ship spun around like a top, and was blown north, south, east and west, and the spray from the churning waves was like a snowstorm that blotted out the sky.

And when the winds had tired of their sport and all the mayhem had died, where do you think Ulysses found himself? Back where he had started, of course, at the island of Aeolus. This time, the King of the Winds would not help him, and it was a long, long time before Ulysses and his men saw Ithaca again.

And perhaps the moral of this sorry tale of greed is, as the ancients would have it, *festina lente*, hasten slowly – for the greater our careless haste to achieve our ends, the longer we may take to reach them.

Fire is so crucial to the survival of the human species that it is inevitable that it was seen as a great boon once in the sole possession of the gods. As in many other myths concerning fire, in this Native American tale from British Columbia, mankind acquires it only through theft – and who better to perform the crime than Coyote, the shape-shifting, miracle-working trickster god of Native American tradition?

COYOTE AND THE THEFT OF FIRE

Above: A Native American wears a coyote pelt. By dressing in the skin of a particular animal, the wearer assumed the identity of that animal.

One evening, as the sun was sinking behind the edge of the world and the wide sky was shot with streaks of purple and red and gold, Coyote stood on a mountaintop and surveyed the land. He saw vast forests of spruce and cedar that clothed the slopes with their velvet blue-black and scented the air with their sticky sap; he saw a river that gouged its way like a current of molten silver through ravines and meadows; and in the far, far distance he saw something he had never seen before – a tiny and flickering light that seemed to have the power to banish the shadows of darkness.

He determined to have a closer look at this marvel and, if he could, to steal it for himself. He gathered together those companions who could help him in his quest – Deer, Bear, Wolf, Fox and several others.

The companions set off on their journey and, after a long time or a short time, they came to the place where the light was. There, in the middle of a large house, flickering tongues of blue and red and gold, as blinding as the rays of the sun, were feeding on a pile of on the fire, but still Coyote was not satisfied.

'How can I dance if my eyes are blind? It is as black as night without moon or stars!' he wailed, and the People fuelled the flames even higher so that the blaze reached above their heads and gave off the heat of a furnace.

'Oh, how hot it is,' cried Coyote's companions, fanning themselves ostentatiously. 'We shall have to go outside among the trees to cool ourselves.'

But Coyote stayed, and danced faster and faster and swished the tails and fringes of his headdress closer and closer to the flames until what he wanted to happen did happen, as he had planned all along. His headdress caught fire, and he ran out, with the Fire People in close pursuit.

Coyote threw the blazing headdress to Deer, who threw it to Bear, who threw it to Wolf, who threw it to Fox, and so on through all the other animals, until at last it came back to Coyote himself. One by one, the Fire People caught up with each animal and killed him. In the end only Coyote was left. But now there was no one to take the fire from Coyote, so he gave the fire to a tree.

And that is how fire came to mankind, and that is why, when people want to make fire, they still kindle it from the wood of trees.

wood that crackled and sputtered, and sending up a column of mist through an opening in the roof. The light that Coyote had seen was fire, and this was the home of the Fire People, who guarded the flame.

'What pleasant company to come upon after our long journey,' said Coyote to the Fire People in his most charming manner. 'May we stay and rest with you awhile, and perhaps later we might play the drum and dance?'

Like all good hosts, the Fire People made their guests welcome, and prepared for a dance in their honour. Coyote made for himself a headdress of pine shavings and bark fringes that reached all the way to the ground.

The Fire People led the dance around the flames, but when the turn came for Coyote and his companions to take part, they complained of the darkness, so the People put more wood

BELOW: AN ENGRAVING OF A COYOTE BY COLONEL H. SMITH (FL. 1833–1845) FROM SIR WILLIAM JARDINE'S *THE NATURALIST'S LIBRARY*. THE COYOTE HELD AN IMPORTANT PLACE IN NATIVE AMERICAN MYTHOLOGY.

CAYGOTIE OF MEXICO.

Prometheus, the hero of this tale, was seen as a benefactor of mankind, and his adventures were set down in the 'Theogony', an epic poem by Hesiod, a Greek poet, based on oral traditions and dating from the eighth century BC. 'Theogony' literally means the 'genealogy of the gods' and the poem was therefore an attempt (the earliest of its kind in Greece) to provide a family tree and life histories for the Greek gods.

PROMETHEUS AND THE THEFT OF FIRE

Zeus, lord of the thunderbolt and the lightning flash, was Master of the gods and he ruled the world from the pinnacle of Mount Olympus. He had achieved this supremacy by dispossessing his own ancestral kin, the Titans. Such family feuding brews a poison that taints the blood for generations to come, and so it was that Zeus found in his cousin Prometheus – the son of the Titan Iapetos, his mother's brother – an arch rival.

Although Prometheus had pretended neutrality during the war with the Titans and had even been admitted by Zeus to the Olympian circle, he harboured in his heart a grudge against the destroyer of his ancestors and his hatred was like an itch that needs scratching. He did not have the fearsome weapons of a sky god such as Zeus, but what he did have – and in abundance – was native-born wit and cunning, and it was with these tools that he sought to undermine his cousin.

Now it so happened one day that all the gods and people of the earth had come together to decide which portion of the ritual sacrifice should be offered to the gods and which to men, and, as Fate would have it, Prometheus has been placed in charge of the division of the sacrificial beast – on this occasion, an enormous ox. With his quick wit, he immediately saw an opportunity to make Zeus look like a fool before the whole world.

Having cut up the animal in his own way, Prometheus began to lay out the portions. On one side, he arranged the succulent flesh, the moist entrails, and all the other tender delicacies that the sacrifice contained, and these he covered with the coarse skin of the beast. On the other side, he placed the carcass and bones, which he disguised under a layer of rich white fat. Then he invited Zeus to choose which portion he considered most fitting as a divine offering. Deceived, Zeus naturally chose the bones. With a flourish of triumph, Prometheus removed the covering of fat:

'Shall the gods eat bones then?' he said with a sneer, exposing Zeus, Lord of Heaven and Earth, as a gullible fool.

Now Zeus knew that Prometheus looked with great favour on mankind, preferring them even to the gods themselves, whom he regarded as the allies of Zeus. This was Prometheus' weak spot, and it gave Zeus an ideal target for his revenge, which was to withhold from mankind the one thing they needed to keep warm and cook their food and light their way ... he would deprive them of fire.

On discovering Zeus' plan, Prometheus instantly went to the island of Lemnos, to the forge of Hephaestos, the Blacksmith of the Gods, where the sacred flame burned, and here he stole a few of the burning embers, secreted them in a fennel stalk, and took this gift of fire to the people of the earth.

Zeus could not take back what had been stolen, but he could punish the thief, and devised for Prometheus a torture of the most exquisite refinement. He had him chained to the crest of Mount Caucasus, and sent an eagle to feed on his liver. All day, the eagle gorged itself, tearing at the liver, and all night, the liver grew again for it, like Prometheus, was immortal. And the next day, the eagle would again come to eat, and the next day and the next, and so on for thirty or thirty thousand years, and Prometheus would doubtless be there still had not Zeus finally taken pity on him and sent the hero Hercules to free him so that he might at last, in peace and reconciliation, join the company of the immortals.

BELOW: THIS ETRUSCAN LIDDED BRONZE CHEST FROM THE 5TH CENTURY BC SHOWS HERCULES FREEING PROMETHEUS.

LIFE & DEATH

The myths in this chapter are concerned with the quest for immortality, that blessed condition enjoyed by the gods but only dimly glimpsed by man. Invariably, when the gift of eternal life is almost within the seeker's grasp, some small act of carelessness causes it to elude him once more.

CHAPTER THREE

of meat and was about to make off with them when Loki, angered by such greed, struck the eagle with his staff, in the middle of the creature's back. But when he tried to retrieve his weapon, he found that the staff was stuck fast to the eagle's back – and his hand in turn was stuck fast to the staff.

The eagle spread out his giant wings and flew off, dragging the helpless Loki along behind him ... but he did not soar so high that Loki was airborne – no, he flew just high enough for the god to be dragged and bumped and bounced along the rocky ground until he was torn and cut and bleeding.

'Have mercy!' Loki screamed. 'I do not want to die – I will do anything ...'

'There is something you can do,' the eagle replied. 'Bring me Idun and her golden apples of youth and I will set you free.'

Loki knew what would happen to the gods if they were deprived of the golden apples, but the important thing now was to save his own skin ... and he would have no skin left to save if this torture was allowed to go on. And so the bargain was struck. The eagle agreed to set Loki free if in seven days' time he promised to bring him Idun and her apples, at an appointed spot in Midgard.

Accordingly, in a week's time, Loki lay in wait for Idun, when he would put his plan into action. When he saw her approaching, her basket of golden apples over her arm, he stepped out before her:

'What a fortunate coincidence to find you here,' he cried, 'for you are the very one I have been waiting for! Come, come with me, I have something to show you ... down in Midgard ... a tree bearing apples of gold as fine – perhaps even finer – than yours!'

Idun was fascinated at this news. There was, of course, no such tree, but this was Loki's way of enticing her away. The trusting goddess, eager to see these other apples so like her own, allowed Loki to lead her out of Asgard, across Bifröst, the flaming rainbow bridge, and down into Midgard ... where the eagle was waiting. He seized the terrified goddess in his great talons and, with a heavy thrumming of wings, flew off with her to his home, the mountain fortress of Thrymheim in Jotunheim, the land of the giants – for, as you have guessed, this was no eagle, but the giant Thjazi in disguise, who wanted the golden apples for himself so that he, and not the gods, might have eternal youth.

Well, what a commotion and a to-do there was up in Asgard when the gods discovered that Idun had gone – and what was even worse was the effect of her missing apples on the gods themselves. As if to make up for being held in check so long, the ravages of age swept over the eternal ones like a dam bursting its wall: all at once their skin was crinkled and papery, their hair thinning and white, their eyes sunk in their sockets, their bones brittle and bent. It was a hideous sight to behold, and the gods were not happy at all.

It did not take Odin long to work out whose hand had been at work here – it was

Loki, as always, troublemaker and trickster. He summoned the god to him and told him that, if he valued his life, he must bring Idun back from wherever she had been taken, however far and however arduous the journey.

Freya, Odin's wife, gave Loki her falcon cloak that she wore to make her magical journeys to the underworld. Loki put it on, and at once all semblance of a man was gone. Where he once had arms, now he had wings; where he once had feet, now he had claws; where he once had a mouth, now he had a beak. He had become a bird, a sharp-eyed falcon. He spread his wings and, with a cry of farewell, began the long flight to Thrymheim, where Idun was being held prisoner.

As luck would have it, when he arrived at the giant's fortress, Thjazi was out hunting so Loki could perform his task unimpeded. He discovered the captive goddess in one of the rooms, and said over her the magic runes, whereupon she was changed into a nut, so small that it would snuggle comfortably in the curve of your palm. Holding the nut in one of his claws, Loki the falcon flew out through the window. And just as he did so, Thjazi returned from his hunting …

When the giant saw that his treasure had been stolen, he donned his eagle cloak to become a bird once more, and set off in pursuit of the thief.

Meanwhile, from a long way away, Odin – who sees all things – had been watching the proceedings and told the gods to build a great fire in Asgard, for Loki was coming. Soon a great pyre was assembled, and all the gods gathered to wait and watch.

With the nut still held tight in his claw, the falcon flew over the mountains of Jotunheim, and he could hear the eagle's cry behind him, coming ever closer.

With the nut still held tight in his claw, the falcon flew over the fields of Midgard, and he could feel the wind from the eagle's wings, coming ever closer.

With the nut still held tight in his claw, the falcon flew past the bridge of Bifröst, and he could feel the nipping of the eagle's claws, coming ever closer.

With the nut still held tight in his claw, the falcon flew into Asgard … and the eagle, coming ever closer behind him, plunged straight into the fire that the gods had made, and was burnt to a cinder … and that was the end of Thjazi, and a bad end it was too!

The gods gathered around the falcon in anticipation, and the falcon dropped the nut from his claw and said over it the magic runes, and, before their very eyes, Idun appeared, with the basket of golden apples over her arms.

And the gods reached into the basket and took of the apples, and they ate and they ate and they ate …

MAGICAL APPLES

The apple is the archetypal, magical fruit of myth and legend. It usually confers wisdom and/or eternal life, and is strongly associated with the Mother Goddess under her various names. Even the well-known wonder tale, Snow White, contains memory traces of the apple's old mythical powers.

APPLES OF THE HESPERIDES

In Greek myth, the apples of immortality belonging to the goddess Hera grew on a paradise island to the far west, guarded, like the tree of Eden, by a serpent called Ladon, and attended by the three sisters known as the Hesperides (see page 152).

APPLE LAND

In Celtic myth, the otherworldly paradise to which Arthur was taken was the island of Avalon, or 'apple land'. He was transported there by no less than three fairy queens – the Triple Goddess in person, or the three Fates. One of these was Morgan le Fay, queen of the island, and equivalent to the Irish Morrigan, Goddess of Fate.

FAIRY FRUIT

In The Ballad of True Thomas, Thomas the Rhymer, the 13th-century rhyming prophet, acquires his powers of foresight when he is given an apple by the Queen of Elfland, which confers on him his 'tongue that ne'er can lee [lie]'.

STAR FRUIT

When an apple is cut in half horizontally (rather than from stalk to base), its pips reveal a pentacle pattern which Gypsies call the 'Star of Knowledge'. This five-pointed star was sacred to the Great Mother Goddess, and remains one of the major occult symbols.

concubine who sleeps on cushions and feeds on sweetmeats. He called to his beasts to wait for him – 'my old companions of the wilderness … do you not know me?' – but to no avail. Enkidu could no longer be one with them, for he had lost his soul's innocence.

He crouched by the harlot's feet, and she completed the task she had been sent to do.

'Enkidu, you are so fine, you are like a god. Why do you wander in the wilderness with the beasts? Come home with me now, come home to Uruk, where the lord Gilgamesh awaits you.'

And Enkidu allowed her to lead him out of freedom and into captivity.

GILGAMESH HAS A DREAM

In his fine palace in Uruk, Gilgamesh was sleeping, but it was a sleep troubled with strange dreams. In his dreams, Gilgamesh was struggling with a man of prodigious strength, one as strong as an army, whom he was unable to vanquish. He consulted his mother, Ninsun, a woman of all-knowing, and she told him

what the dream foretold. He would indeed fight a powerful opponent, but in the end their rivalry would cease and this adversary would become his closest companion.

And so it was. Enkidu arrived at the palace, and he and Gilgamesh grappled together and opposed their strength, one against the other. But when all their fury was spent, they put aside their enmity and became the best of friends. Adorned in jewels and royal robes, Enkidu sat at Gilgamesh's table, by his left hand, and the people praised him and the princes of the world came to kiss his feet. Together Enkidu and Gilgamesh feasted, together they hunted the desert lion and the wild ox, together they spent their days. They loved each other as a brother loves his brother and they were seldom parted.

GILGAMESH FIGHTS A MONSTER

All continued awhile in this peaceful and happy manner until, one day, Enkidu had a vision, a premonition of what was to come. A being with sombre face and eagle's claws lifted him and bore him skyward, then cast him into the netherworld, into the house of dust from which place none who enters ever returns.

When Gilgamesh heard of Enkidu's vision, he prayed to Shamash, asking what the strange omen might mean and making to the god an offering of a pot of jet and honey, and a pot of lapis-lazuli and butter. In answer, Shamash told Gilgamesh that he must go to fight Khumbaba the Strong, Khumbaba the King of the Cedar Mountain.

Now this Khumbaba was a terrifying monster: his voice was like the storm, his breath was like the wind, and his mouth was the mouth of the gods. He had been placed on the Cedar Mountain by none other than Enlil himself, Lord of the Air and Master of Fate, to guard the forest there.

Despite the dangers of the errand, despite every protestation from his people, from the elders, and even from his mother, Gilgamesh was determined to face the monster, and he set off with Enkidu his faithful friend, as always, by his side.

The two friends travelled onward for the space of twenty thousand hours, for that was the distance of Khumbaba's dwelling from Uruk. When they arrived at the forest of cedars, Gilgamesh made preparations for the battle; he consulted the omens, making offerings to the dead and chanting the funeral chant. Then he called on all the gods to help him, and the gods unleashed on Khumbaba all the elements, and in the end the monster conceded defeat.

And this was a great victory, yet from it great sorrow would come.

GILGAMESH ANGERS ISHTAR

Victorious Gilgamesh, with his friend Enkidu, returned to Uruk. There he washed the battle stains off his body, perfumed his skin with oils and unguents, donned a fresh robe and jewelled girdle, placed his golden crown on his head, and emerged from his palace, fine and handsome and glowing with glory.

And this was how the goddess Ishtar saw him, when she looked down with languorous eyes on high-walled Uruk.

'Oh, Gilgamesh,' she cried, 'you are beautiful as a god. Come with me and be my lover. Come to my dwelling where the perfumed cedars grow, and I will place you above all the kings and princes and lords of the world. Come with me, and I shall give you a chariot of lapis lazuli and gold. Come with me …'

But Gilgamesh hardened his heart against her soft words of flattery, for he remembered the fate of others whom the goddess had loved.

'I will not come with thee, Ishtar, Queen of Heaven, for I know thy fickle and treacherous heart. Didst thou not love Tammuz, the one called the Gardener, and yet thou struck him down? Didst thou not love the lion, yet dug for him seven times seven pits? Didst thou not love the stallion, yet broke him under the halter and

---

BELOW: THE LOVE GODDESS ISHTAR WHOM GILGAMESH SPURNED, AT HIS PERIL. THE RAINBOW WAS SAID TO BE HER 'NECKLACE', AND HER SEVEN VEILS ITS COLOURS.

Gilgamesh went at once to consult the wise one, and explain his quest for immortality, to which Uta-Napishtim replied:

'Does a house stand for ever? Does the corn grow for ever in the fields? To everything, there is a beginning and an ending, and so it is with the life of man. The length of time a man may live is measured by the gods, and each must accept his fate when it comes.'

And to prove the truth of his words, he proposed a test to Gilgamesh:

'Sleep, it is said, is the twin of death. If thou canst resist the one for a span of six days and seven nights, then perchance thou might escape the other.'

But hardly were the words out of his mouth than Gilgamesh – exhausted from the exertions of his long and arduous journey – collapsed into the deepest of slumbers, so hungry was he for rest.

'See how the brave hero succumbs,' said Uta-Napishtim scornfully to his wife. 'Sleep devours him as a wave swallows the sand.'

GILGAMESH PLUCKS THE PLANT OF YOUTH

But Uta-Napishtim's wife felt sorry for Gilgamesh and persuaded her husband, before Gilgamesh departed, to tell him of a magical plant that could twist the thread of destiny, for it had the power to restore youth to whoever ate of it. The plant was called 'The-old-man-becomes-young' and it grew at the bottom of the Sea of Oblivion.

For a second time Urshanabi ferried Gilgamesh out into the middle of the Sea. Tying stones to his feet to weigh him down, Gilgamesh plunged deep into the waters – which could not harm him now – and there on the sea-bed he espied the thorny plant of which Uta-Napishtim had spoken. He tore it up by the roots, removed the stones from his feet, rose to the surface, and was returned by the Boatman to the shores of the land of the living, with the prize he had come all this way to find grasped tightly in his hand.

Gilgamesh was triumphant. He had in his possession the secret of eternal youth, and with it he would regain all the vigour of his younger days.

But Fate steps in when men least expect it, tossing their schemes to the winds like so much chaff in a winnowing basket.

GILGAMESH LOSES ALL

On his return journey to Uruk, Gilgamesh stopped by a clear spring, to quench his thirst and wash the dust of his travels from his body, laying the Plant of Youth down on the bank. But while he was thus occupied, a serpent, enticed by the Plant's heady fragrance, darted out of her hiding place, stole the herb and ate

LEFT: THE ASTROLOGICAL SIGN SCORPIO WAS RELATED TO THE SCORPION MEN WHO SERVED SIDURI SABITU WHO 'SAT ON THE THRONE OF THE SEA'. SHE WAS IDENTIFIED WITH THE BABYLONIAN SCORPION GODDESS ISHARA OF THE SEA.

THE SERPENT OF REGENERATION

The symbolism associated with the snake makes it one of the greatest mythic archetypes of all, for it lies at the epicentre of creation, where life and death meet. Its apparently miraculous ability to slough its skin when it has outworn it and thus be born anew is proof that it possesses the secret of immortality. The way it moves, coiling and undulating, also links it with the spiral – an ancient symbol going back to prehistoric times that represents the descent into death and the ascent of rebirth – and with the wave, symbol of the great womb of the sea. Since it is privy to the divine mysteries of existence, the snake is the natural guardian of the Tree of Life and the Fruits of Immortality and All-Knowing.

NINGIZZIDA

Over 1,000 years before the writing of the book of Genesis, with its trouble-making snake that lurks in the garden eastward of Eden, the Sumerians knew the sacred serpent as the god Ningizzida, consort of the Mother Goddess and Lord of the Tree of Truth.

ANANTA THE INFINITE

Ananta was the cosmic serpent of Hindu myth in whose coils the gods spent their periodic interludes of sleep or death.

MEHEN THE ENVELOPER

Mehen was the Egyptian serpent goddess who enfolded the sun god Ra during his regular, nightly sojourn in the underworld, the realm of death.

KUNDALINI

The serpent coiled around the Tree of Immortality like a stream of rising sap epitomizes the surging life spirit within the tree. Similarly, the snake imaged as Kundalini, coiled in the pelvis in the lowest chakra of the body, symbolizes the serpent power which Kundalini yoga aims to awake.

ABOVE: LIKE ITS COUSIN IN EDEN, THE SNAKE WAS THE SNEAK-THIEF THAT SNATCHED FROM GILGAMESH THE DIVINE PRIVILEGE OF ETERNAL LIFE THAT WAS SO NEARLY HIS.

it and, in so doing, sloughed off her old skin and was born anew, lithe and supple and young as on the day of her birth.

When Gilgamesh saw what the serpent had done, he sat down and he wept and wept. And his bitter tears coursed like the streams of the mountain down his cheeks.

It was then that Gilgamesh saw his hopes vanish, like so many phantoms in the mist. It was then that he knew he had wearied himself to no purpose, that all his efforts had been in vain, that through his own carelessness he had given away his peerless boon, his pearl without equal. It was then that he knew, with a bitterness that almost broke his heart, that the gift of his heart's desire, so nearly within his grasp, had been lost to the serpent for ever – the Serpent of Regeneration who has taken to herself alone, for now and for all time, man's place in the Paradise Garden of Eternity.

In this Maori story, Maui, the deity known in various guises right across Polynesia, is up to his old tricks again. But even Maui is not clever enough to outwit death …

MAUI AND THE WATERS OF LIFE

One evening, Maui was walking along the seashore, just as the sun was setting. After his exertions of travelling across the sky all day, the sun's power was rapidly fading and Maui watched as, in a final show of glory, he burned up and died, his blood-red body sinking into the ocean.

But the next morning, when Maui looked at the eastern horizon, the sun was back again, looking as bright and fresh as a newborn babe! And it was just the same with the moon. At night, she rose and in the morning she died, only to rise again the next night.

This was indeed a wondrous wonder. What could possibly explain it all? Maui thought long and hard, and at last the truth dawned on him. When the sun and the moon died and disappeared into the ocean, they went to bathe in the waters of life, and this was

ABOVE: MAUI GETS HIS COME-UPPANCE, AS THE GODDESS WHOSE WOMB HE TRIES TO RE-ENTER PREPARES TO CRUSH HIM BETWEEN HER THIGHS. THE CARVING WAS PART OF A DOOR LINTEL FROM A MAORI MEETING HOUSE.

FROM WOMB TO TOMB

In this story Hine-nui-te-po is primarily the taker of life and mother of the dead, but she also has the power to renew life. The idea of such a creator-destroyer goddess is common to many cultures, which see life and death not as opposites but as two sides of the same coin. Because she is the source of existence itself, what she gives out she naturally takes back into herself in the unending cycle of death and rebirth – her womb is also the 'tomb'.

Above: By laughing at the sight of Maui, the fantail woke Hine-nui-te-po and became indirectly responsible for the existence of death.

why they were always reborn the following day.

Well, if the sun and the moon could die and come back to life, why not Maui too? And if he could overcome death, so could all of mankind. Maui knew exactly what he had to do. He would have to go back, through the way that children come into the world, into the womb of Hine-nui-te-po – the goddess of death and renewal – where the waters of life were stored. There he would drink the eternal waters and return to the world by the way he had come.

Maui set off for the underworld where the goddess lived. Following behind him fluttered a group of little birds, among them the fantail, anxious to see what mischief the great trickster would be getting up to this time. Maui's task was a dangerous one, and he knew it would require all his cunning and stealth if he was to achieve his end. He waited until Hine-nui-te-po was asleep, then he approached her and placed himself between her legs so that he might enter her womb.

With a good deal of squeezing and squashing and turning from side to side, he pushed his head inside her body and then his shoulders, first the right one, then the left. So far, so good, and Maui had managed to do all this without the goddess even so much as stirring. Next for his chest …

Now all this time, the little birds that had followed him had been watching silently, without uttering so much as a cheep or chirrup. But the ridiculous sight of Maui's head and shoulders and his wriggling and writhing body being slowly swallowed by Hine-nui-te-po became too much for the fantail, who could contain himself no longer.

He burst out laughing … and his laughter woke Hine-nui-te-po. When the goddess saw what the impudent Maui was up to, she was not in the least amused; she slammed her legs together and he was well and truly crushed.

And that was the end of Maui's little adventure. He never did manage to steal immortality for mankind and that is why, when people die, they go to live with Hine-nui-te-po for ever and they do not return.

EARTH AND SEA

The Creator-destroyer Goddess is usually seen as a personification of the ocean or the earth, those submarine and subterranean 'underworlds' out of which life arises and into which life dies back.

This Pawnee story, featuring Tirawa the Creator, describes how death was accidentally introduced to the world through a foolish act of theft. The Pawnee lived on the Great Plains of North America.

LIGHTNING AND THE SACK OF STORMS

Long, long ago, so the tale is told, Tirawa the Great Spirit called a meeting of all the gods and appointed to each a place in the sky – Shakura the sun to the east, Pah the moon to the west, the Pole Star to the north, the Star of Death to the south – and gave to each an appointed task and time, telling Bright Star to shine at dusk and Big Star to shine at dawn … but that is not this story.

And a second tale is told of how Tirawa made the Clouds, the Winds, Lightning and Thunder, and how he dressed them in buffalo hides and mocassins and put them in the care of Bright Star … but that is not this story.

And a third tale is told of how all the Clouds and the Winds and Thunder and Lightning assembled in heaven, and how Tirawa dropped a pebble between them and they parted to reveal a vast ocean far below, and how Tirawa armed the gods and they smote the waters and the waters parted and the earth appeared … but that is not this story.

This story tells of how the wolf brought Death into the world.

It all began one day when Tirawa looked down at this new earth that had come out of the waters, and decided to send Lightning down to explore it. Bright Star gave Lightning the sack of storms in which she had also enclosed all the stars of the different constellations that flee before Big Star at dawn.

Well, Lightning had a fascinating time poking and prodding around in this beautiful new world, stretching out his long, crooked arms to touch the mountaintops, sliding his sinewy fingers down among the branches of the trees. When at last he had travelled to all four quarters of the world and seen all there was to see, he put down the sack of storms he had been carrying, took out the stars, and began to hang them carefully in the sky, paying great attention to their placing.

But one of the stars, whose name was Coyote Cheater because it fools the coyote into believing it is the morning star, was jealous of Bright Star's power over the elements, and wanted the sack of storms for himself. But, fixed there in the sky as he was, he could not come down to steal it himself, so he looked around to see if there was any living thing that could perpetrate the theft for him … and there, loping through a forest, he saw a lone wolf.

'Psst!' Coyote Cheater called, 'Up here!'

The wolf looked up.

'I have something I want you to do for me …' and with false promises of rewards to come, Coyote Cheater persuaded the wolf to steal the sack of storms.

Well, of course, no sooner had the foolish wolf lifted the sack in his jaws than the end fell open and all the storms roared out, and went howling and screaming over the plains and through the forests, looking for their master Lightning. And when they could not find him, and when they discovered who it was that had let them out of the bag, they turned on the wolf and in their frenzy tore him limb from limb, and thus the wolf was the first creature on earth to die.

And that is how Death came into the world … and it will never leave until the sun goes black and the moon goes red and the Star of Death rules the sky, and when that time comes the souls of the dead will be made into stars and they will fly along the Milky Way, for that is the path to heaven.

CANINE COMPANIONS

Like that other member of the canine family, the dog, the wolf was strongly associated with death and reincarnation, perhaps because, like the dog, it was a hunter, killer and eater of the dead. In ancient Egypt, Anubis the jackal god and guardian of the afterworld was identified with an older wolf-god originating in central Asia, known as Up-Uat or 'The Opener of the Way' – in other words, the intermediary between the worlds of the living and the dead. In certain Native American traditions, another canine – the coyote – was also 'The Opener of the Way', because he helped Mother Earth to give birth to the human race by scratching an opening in her side.

MAGIC &
MYSTERIES

The craft of the weaver and spinner and the art of the bard and minstrel are the subjects of the following myths. These, though, are no ordinary artisans but possessors of fairy secrets, wizardly power and divine enlightenment, a privileged band who have divined the mysteries of existence.

CHAPTER FOUR

Odin is again the chief protagonist in this Norse myth, which makes a clear link between poetry – the power of the Word – and wisdom in its grandest sense, as a quality of 'all-knowingness'. The magical elixir concocted in this tale makes an interesting comparison with the Mead of Inspiration in the Taliesin story on page 102, likewise brewed in a cauldron.

ODIN AND THE MEAD OF ALL-KNOWING

ABOVE: ODIN RIDES THE SKY LIKE THE SHAMAN OF THE UNIVERSE ACCOMPANIED BY HIS RAVENS, THOUGHT AND MEMORY. *PAGE 90*: 'ORPHEUS IN THE UNDERWORLD BEFORE PLUTO AND PROSERPINA.'

In the song of the bard is the truth of the seer, and of all the great bards and seers that have ever lived, the greatest was Allfather Odin … but what, you ask, was the secret of his mystical power? The secret lay in a magical drink made from spittle and honey and blood.

Listen …

Once upon at time, there were two races of gods. There were the Aesir and the Vanir, and the Aesir and the Vanir went to war with each other, and when their hostilities were over, they came together and, as a mark that there was no more ill feeling between them, they each and every one spat into a great jar, and from the mingling of their spittle came a man. The man was called Kvasir and he was a great sage, the wisest man in all the nine worlds of creation.

Wherever Kvasir went he dispensed his wisdom, and it was not long before news of this paragon reached the ears of two dwarves, brothers by the names of Fjalar and Galar, and a more hideous and unsavoury pair you could not imagine. Now as we all know, envy sows the seed of evil, and these dwarves could not bear the thought of anyone possessing something they did not, so they devised a plan to ensnare Kvasir. They invited him to a banquet in their underground cavern – and it was not the kind of affair that you or I would wish to attend, of that I can assure you, for the cave was a most unwelcoming place for a feast, being cold and dripping and dank, but at least the dishes on which the food was served were of solid gold encrusted with jewels, for dwarves are known to be great hoarders of treasure, so that went a little way to make up for the dreariness of the setting ... but to continue with the tale ...

As soon as the other guests had left and Fjalar and Galar had Kvasir alone, they led him to a chamber where they had prepared two jars, Son and Bodn, and a great cauldron, Odrorir, and there they raised their daggers and plunged them into Kvasir's flesh – again and again and again in an orgy of killing. As the daggers pierced his body, Kvasir's blood gushed out like a spurting spring and ran into Son and Bodn and Odrorir, until in the end he had no blood left and lay, drained and lifeless, on the cold stone floor of the cave.

When the gods sent to enquire after Kvasir, the dwarves said that he had choked on his own words, for such words of wisdom were too rich a diet for anyone. And then, furtively and in secret, they mixed honey with the blood, and left the mixture in Son and Bodn and Odrorir to bubble and ferment and brew until it had turned into the most miraculous concoction – it became hydromel, the magical mead with the power to confer the gift of poetry and all-knowing on any who tasted of it. But the dwarves told no one the secret of the honeyed draught which they kept hidden deep in their underground cave.

Some time later, Fjalar and Galar again became hosts, this time to a pair of giants, Gilling and his wife, and naturally, because of their irascible and impatient natures, it was not long before they fell to quarrelling with their

BELOW: THE REMAINS OF A CAULDRON FOUND IN DENMARK. LIKE ODRORIR IN THIS TALE, THE CAULDRON WAS A POTENT SYMBOL THROUGHOUT INDO-EUROPEAN MYTHOLOGY BEING SEEN AS THE FOUNT OF LIFE AND ENLIGHTENMENT.

long before they fell to quarrelling with their guests. Now as we all know, anger sows the seeds of transgression, and so it was that this whole event ended in the most unseemly manner, with the dwarves again committing murder and killing both Gilling and his wife, and I will spare you the ugly details – just suffice it to say that the deed was done with a deal more violence than was called for, and not a little pleasure.

When Gilling and his wife did not return home, their son Suttung set off to look for them. Challenged as to the whereabouts of his father and mother, Fjalar and Galar made all kinds of excuses – yes, they had been expecting them but they hadn't arrived; no, now that they recalled, they had arrived but had left early; yes, they had said something about going for a walk by the sea and the dwarves had warned them to watch out for the treacherous tides; and so on and so forth, but Suttung was not convinced and extracted the truth from them, and was just about to kill them when Fjalar and Galar cried out, 'Wait! We have a treasure, a magic draught that no one else in all the nine worlds knows of – and it can be yours! Only spare our lives!'

And so it was that the hydromel, the mead of poetry and all-knowing, passed from the hands of Fjalar and Galar into the hands of Suttung the giant. Suttung took Son and Bodn and Odrorir and secreted them deep in the heart of his mountain fortress, Hnitbjorg, and set his daughter Gunnlöd to guard them.

Now Suttung was not as secretive as the previous owners of the mead, and news of the miraculous brew soon reached the ears of Odin, and the Allfather decided to bring the hydromel home to Asgard, where the gods lived – for after all, Kvasir, whose blood made up a large part of the elixir, was himself fashioned from the spittle of the gods.

Odin knew that the giant would not willingly hand over the hydromel to him: this quest demanded underhand methods. So, in disguise, he set off for the home of Baugi, the brother of Suttung, and there, by a ruse, killed all nine of his thralls, the serfs who worked his land, so that Baugi had no farmhands left.

'What am I to do now?' wailed the disgruntled giant. 'Who will I get to till the fields? And there's the corn to reap! And the hedges to cut! How could anyone be so inconsiderate as to go and get themselves killed – does no one ever think of me? What am I to do now? Oh, it is

POETIC POWERS

Unlike the undervalued and often impoverished figures they have become in modern society, poets once belonged to a priestly class of at least the same rank as kings, and were revered as 'magicians of the Word'.

THE SKALD

In Scandinavia, such poets were known as 'skalds', and what they foretold in their songs would come true. A great 'skald' had the ability, through his funerary ballads, to speak to the Goddess of Death herself.

THE OLLAMH

The 'ollamh' (pronounced ollave) was an Irish bard of the highest order, who had to train for many years to achieve his station. Such was the power of his words that he could, by means of a 'satire' or cursing air (the original meaning of the word), induce boils to break out on the face of his victim, or other such physical unpleasantries – and could even kill rats by hurling at them one of his magical insults.

ENCHANTMENT

A connection between the concept of the spell – the utterance of words that have magical power to effect change – and the sung words of the bardic singer may be found in the word 'enchant', which literally means to bewitch someone by 'singing them in' (en-chant-ing) under the influence of a spell.

true, a farmer's life is indeed a thankless one!'

'I will till your fields, and reap your corn, and cut your hedges,' said a voice. 'Although I am only one man, I have the strength of nine. Let me do this work for you, and all I ask in return is one drink of your brother's mead.' And that is how Odin, under the false name of Bolverk, came into the service of Baugi.

Now Baugi knew that his brother would never give anyone even the merest drop of the hydromel, but his need for help on the farm was more pressing than his desire for honesty, so he said nothing. And when the day came to give Odin his wages and Suttung adamantly refused him access to the magic draught, Baugi was persuaded, by the force of Odin's tongue, to bore a hole right through the mountain of Hnitbjorg to the room where the mead was stored. No sooner was this narrow tunnel made than Odin changed himself into a snake and, quicker than a flash of inspiration, slithered through it into the chamber in the middle of the mountain where Gunnlöd sat guarding Son and Bodn and Odrorir.

Straightaway, Odin resumed his normal appearance – not that of the humble farmhand Bolverk, but that of the Lord of Asgard in all his glory. Well, Gunnlöd had never clapped eyes on anyone so handsome before, and, it must be said, sitting watching over two jars and a cauldron all day cannot have been very entertaining, so she gladly welcomed the diversion Odin offered.

Oh, and then how Odin sweet-talked her, and how he flattered her, and how he billed and cooed in her ear! And he did his job well, for in the end the poor giantess was so befuddled with love, so awash with desire, that she would have agreed to anything. Odin lay with her for three nights, and when the time came for him to leave he asked, as a parting gift, for a drink from each of the three containers that held the hydromel – 'One for each night we have lain together ...'

The besotted Gunnlöd granted him his wish, and Odin drank from Son and he drank from Bodn and he drank from Odrorir, and when he had finished drinking he had drunk all three containers dry. Then, holding the hydromel in his mouth, he changed into an eagle and flew off in the direction of Asgard, with Suttung, also transformed into an eagle, in hot pursuit.

When the gods caught sight of the two eagles approaching, they quickly laid out a vast array of bowls and jars, as many as they could find. As Odin dived into the safety of Asgard his pursuer gave up the chase, and Odin spat out the contents of his mouth into all the receptacles prepared for him, and in this way all the hydromel was saved – well, not quite all of it, for in his hurried flight home, Odin had let fall a few small drops, but it was too inconsequential a portion to bother about. And that small spillage of the mead of poetry, of the elixir of all-knowing, fell to Midgard, the land of men, and it is the inferior residue that has, ever since, inspired all the bad poets on earth.

Orpheus, the chief character of this classical Greek myth, has an excellent pedigree. He was the son of the solar god Apollo, who was also god of music, poetry and prophesy, and of the muse Calliope, who inspired epic poetry. Compare the bardic skills of Orpheus with those of Odin on pages 92–95, and his ability to continue talking even after his head was severed from his body with that of Brân on pages 170–175.

ORPHEUS AND THE MUSIC OF ENCHANTMENT

There was once a great bard by the name of Orpheus, whose skills were famed far and wide. When he ran his fingers over the strings of his lyre and raised his voice in song, all the world stopped to listen. The birds ceased their trilling, the wind ceased its whistling, the lion lay down with the lamb, the wolf with the kid, and even the trees, it is said, uprooted themselves so as to come closer, for every living thing was stilled to a hush, spellbound by the magical music Orpheus played.

When Orpheus sailed with Jason on his quest to find the fleece of gold, it was again the power of his lyre that vanquished the dangers of the journey. Hearing his song, the Argo, Jason's ship, slid into the waters of its own accord; hearing his song, the dragon guarding the golden fleece was lullabied to sleep;

ABOVE: ORPHEUS ENCHANTS THE ANIMALS WITH THE MUSIC OF HIS LYRE. SUCH WAS ITS BEWITCHING POWER THAT IT CAUSED PREY AND PREDATOR TO LIE DOWN TOGETHER, AND EVEN INANIMATE OBJECTS WERE NOT IMMUNE TO ITS CHARMS.

hearing his song, the Sirens – whose own voices were bewitching enough to lure sailors to their deaths – lost their power to charm.

In the groves where Orpheus made his music lived numerous nymphs, and one of them was called Eurydice. As time went by, Orpheus found himself falling more and more deeply in love with her, and at last they were married. Orpheus did not believe it was possible to be so happy, and his songs now were so joyful that the very stars in heaven danced.

And then one day, tragedy struck. As Eurydice was running through a meadow, she was bitten on the ankle by a poisonous snake, and died instantly. Like many before and since, she was at once transported to the underworld, where she became one of the Shades, the ghostly host of the dead.

ABOVE: ORPHEUS CLASPS THE LIFELESS EURYDICE, IN A PAINTING BY
FREDERICK WATTS. BY NOW, SHE HAS BECOME ONE OF THE 'SHADES',
THAT HOST OF THE DEAD THAT INHABITS THE UNDERWORLD.

Orpheus looked everywhere for her and, when he could not find her, he realized what had happened. But he could not bear to be parted from his beloved Eurydice, so he resolved to go before Hades and Persephone, the King and Queen of the Dead, and play for them his music of enchantment in an attempt to persuade them to release his wife.

And so the son of shining Apollo made his way down, deep, deep into the earth, and what a desolate journey it was. He passed through the Grove of Persephone, where black poplars and sterile willows grow; he fed a honey cake to Cerberus, the three-headed watchdog of hell; he saw the streams of death, that flow like currents of tears through the underworld – the Acheron, river of affliction, the Cocytus, river of lamentation, the Lethe, river of forgetfulness, and the Styx, that winds its course nine times around the dark kingdom. He travelled in the boat of Charon the ferryman and, finally, he arrived at his destination and at last stood before the King and Queen of the dead.

It was then that he picked up his lyre and lifted his voice and began to sing, and his song was of such poignant beauty that it would have broken your heart to hear it. As the strains of his music wafted through the halls of hell, all the shades forgot their punishments and fell silent. Tantalus stopped trying to quench his thirst in the lake that shrank from him every time he stooped to drink from it; Sisyphus stopped trying to push a rock to the top of a hill only to have it roll down again; and the Danaids stopped trying to fill a broken jar with water from a sieve.

There was even a tear in the eye of Persephone and, because the Queen of the Dead was not wholly hard-hearted, she granted Orpheus his wish: he might take Eurydice back with him, but on one condition – he must at no point look back at her until they had left the underworld completely.

This seemed an easy enough condition, and Orpheus was overjoyed. He began the journey home, in the knowledge that Eurydice was following close behind. They went back by the same way he had come – back past Cerberus, back over the water with Charon, back through the grove of lifeless trees.

They were nearly out now – Orpheus could see a glimmer of sunlight. He could hardly wait to hold Eurydice in his arms again. But, just as he stepped across the exit from the underworld, he couldn't resist a peek, just a tiny peek, to make sure that his beloved was still there behind him … and as he did so, all he saw was Eurydice holding out her pleading arms to him as she faded back into the shadowy land of death. Orpheus cursed himself for his foolishness. If only he had waited just a moment more … but 'if only' is always too late. Orpheus would never see Eurydice again.

After this, all the joy went out of his song and he became a recluse, haunting lonely places in the mountains. For seven months, so the people said, they could still hear the faint echoes of Orpheus' mournful music borne to them by the North Wind, but after that there was silence. It was rumoured that he had killed himself or – worse still – that he had been torn to pieces by Maenads, wild women who roamed the mountains, and who were infuriated by his single-minded love for his dead wife.

Whatever the truth of his death, what is known is that unnamed hands flung his head and his lyre onto the river Hebrus, and the river carried them out to the sea and the sea carried them to the island of Lesbos, where his head became lodged in a rock. And although it was detached from his body, it still had the power of speech, and for many a long year the miraculous talking head of the bard delivered oracles to all who came to consult it. The lyre, meanwhile, was kept in a temple and became a sacred object of great veneration.

And it is said that ever since the day that the lyre and head of Orpheus arrived on Lesbos, the birds there have sung more sweetly than they do anywhere else in Greece.

BELOW: ORPHEUS BEFORE THE THRONE OF HADES, KING OF THE SUBTERRANEAN LAND OF THE DEAD, WHERE THE BARD HAS COME TO PLAY FOR THE RELEASE OF EURYDICE.

THE GOD ON THE GALLOWS

Odin had a passion for wisdom and knowledge of magic. The source for this most strange of his adventures is the poem called 'Havamal', in the manuscript known as the 'Codex Regius', which was composed between AD 900 and 1050.

Odin was the wisest of the gods and the getting of wisdom was his greatest desire. It was for wisdom that he had sacrificed an eye in exchange for one drink from the Spring of Enlightenment guarded by the talking head of the wise god Mimir. And whenever anyone saw Odin, they would know him for who he was, by his one eye and his broad-brimmed hat and his ravens, Huginn and Muninn, Thought and Memory, ever by his side.

But of all the deeds done and sacrifices made by Odin in the pursuit of the gift of all-knowing the greatest was when he surrendered his own life, hanging himself from Yggdrasil, in order to gain understanding of the mysteries that are known only to the dead.

This Yggdrasil was the mighty ash tree that framed the universe. It had always been there. Its first root burrowed into Asgard, home of the gods, and beneath it was the Well of Urd, guarded by the three Norns, the goddesses of destiny, whose names were Fate, Being and Necessity. Its second root delved into Jotunheim, the land of the giants, and beneath this root bubbled the Spring of Mimir, from which Odin had drunk. Its third root grew into Niflheim, land of the dead, and beneath this sprang the Spring of Hvergelmir, the source of eleven rivers. In the uppermost branches sat an eagle with a hawk sitting between its eyes;

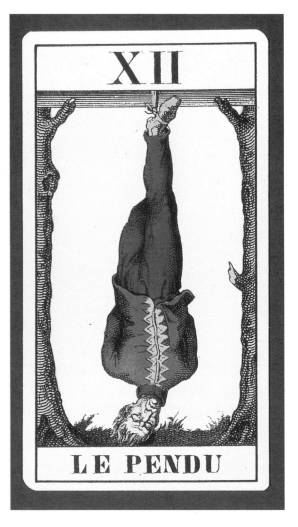

ABOVE: THE HANGED MAN OF THE TAROT SUGGESTS A DEATH OF THE OLD TO MAKE WAY FOR THE NEW, AND EVOKES ODIN'S SACRIFICE.

below the lowest root lurked the dragon Nidhogg, for ever gnawing at the wood; and ceaselessly, up and down between the two, ran Ratatosk the squirrel. Yggdrasil gave shelter and sustenance to all life, and honeydew dripped from its branches.

It was to this great tree, then, that Odin came one day, in his quest for wisdom. Wounding himself with his own spear, he suspended himself from the branches, offering himself to himself like the human victims who in their turn were sacrificed to him.

And as the god hung there, the wind came and blew and shook the branches of the tree, and Odin swung back and forth, like a corpse swinging on the gallows. One night went by, two nights, three, then four, and so on until nine whole days and nights had gone by, and in all that time no one had come to soothe his pain or relieve his hunger; no one brought him bread to eat, nor drink from a drinking horn.

At last, feeling himself passing into death, Odin happened to look down and saw, inscribed on an object far below him, magical letters known as runes. Summoning his last drop of strength and all his willpower, he reached down and lifted up the runes, but the effort caused him to cry out in agony and fall back. He maintained his frail grip on the letters nevertheless and, as he did so, a miraculous thing happened; he felt new vigour tingling in his veins, new vitality returning. The runes had restored him to life.

After this, one thing quickly led to another: the more words he read the more words he could read, and the more words he could read the more deeds he could do. He learned nine songs that came from his

mother's brother; he learned charms to cure the sick and to take away pain and sorrow; he learned secrets that the healer should know; he learned spells to disarm his enemy and free himself from lock and chain; he learned how to deflect the arrows of his foe and to give strength to his comrades in battle; he learned enchantments to quench fire, to still the wind, to uproot hatred, to confound witches, and to turn away spells worked against him; he learned how to bring the hanged man back to life and how to prevent a child falling in battle; he learned how to bring power to the gods and glory to the elves, all of whom he could name one by one, and how to gain more wisdom for himself; he learned how to win the love of a woman and undying devotion in a maid; and the last charm he learned was a secret, which he would never tell save to his own sister or to a woman with whom he lay in bed, for the most powerful magic is that which we keep to ourselves. And when Odin had learned all the charms, they were eighteen in number, and with the songs and the charms together, the runes numbered three times nine.

And that is how Odin gave his own life in the getting of wisdom, and how he became the wisest of all the gods.

LEFT: A STONE FROM LAEBORG, DENMARK, INSCRIBED WITH RUNES. THE SECRET CODE OF THE RUNES RESTORED ODIN TO LIFE, AND CONFERRED ON HIM MAGICAL KNOWLEDGE.

The 'coming of Taliesin' is recorded in the 'Mabinogion' (from mabinogi, 'instruction for young bards'), a collection of legends from the tradition of the Welsh-speaking Celts. The bard himself seems to be a mythic or semi-mythic figure rather like Arthur. His use of the phrase 'I have been' is, like the 'I am' of the Irish bard Amairgen on first setting foot on Irish soil, richly symbolic for it signifies the speaker's transcendence as an eternal spirit existing outside of and yet within everything throughout all of time.

TALIESIN OF THE SHINING BROW

Once, in the days when the wolf roamed the forest, the lark sang in the sky, and the world of man was filled with mysteries and marvels, there lived a woman of wisdom and power called Cerridwen. Cerridwen had a young son who went by the name of Afagddu. Sadly, to the great dismay of his mother, the boy excelled neither in appearance nor in wit; in short, he was ugly as well as stupid. If his plainness offended his mother, his lack of wisdom pained her even more, and she resolved to use all the magical skills at her disposal to give him the gift of all-knowing.

She set about her task without delay.

Turning to her books of faery arts, she pored over the pages long and hard until, at last, among the secrets of Virgil the Gaul, she discovered a spell for making a Cauldron of Inspiration. Many different ingredients were needed for the magical brew – spices, incense, silver, wheat, honey, berries and herbs, picked

ABOVE: THE FAMOUS GUNDERSTRUP CAULDRON, FOUND IN A BOG NEAR ROEVEMOSEN, AARS, DENMARK, REVEALS MUCH CELTIC IMAGERY. THE CAULDRON HELD A KEY PLACE IN CELTIC LORE AND FEATURED IN VARIOUS GUISES IN CELTIC MYTH.

at the moment of greatest potency according to the placing of the stars. All these things Cerridwen stirred into her Cauldron. Then – as the book instructed – she set it over the fire to boil for a year and a day. At the ending of that day, marked by the rising of the moon, the first three drops from the Cauldron of Inspiration would yield the gift of all-knowing to whoever tasted them.

Having prepared the mixture, Cerridwen ordered her servant boy Gwion Bach to tend the Cauldron, to stir it well and to keep it boiling for its appointed time. The boy duly obeyed. Day and night he sat by the side of the great stewpot, stirring diligently as the brew

BELOW: DOUBLE, DOUBLE TOIL AND TROUBLE, FIRE BURN AND CAULDRON BUBBLE: CERRIDWEN CONCOCTS HER MAGICAL BREW IN HER CAULDRON OF INSPIRATION.

became ever more powerful. At last, when the year and a day was nearing its end, three drops of the potion accidentally splashed onto the boy's finger – the three drops that were meant for Afagddu, Cerridwen's son.

Without thinking, Gwion Bach licked his finger clean, and the gift of all-knowing became his. He knew all that had been and all that would be. He knew what the wind murmured and what the crow foretold. He knew why foam is white and why sea is salt, why the echo answers itself and how many drops there are in a shower of rain. He knew why a mother loves a child and what hopes and fears hide in the hearts of men. And he knew – as surely as the sun shines by day and the moon by night – that Cerridwen intended to kill him.

He quickly leapt from his stool and, as he did so, the Cauldron shattered into a hundred pieces, for all that was left in it was deadly poison. The cracking of the Cauldron alerted Cerridwen, and she gave chase.

Gwion Bach became a hare in the field. But Cerridwen became a hound on the scent, and the chase went on.

Gwion Bach became a fish in the water. But Cerridwen became an otter on the wave, and the chase went on.

Gwion Bach became a dove in the air. But Cerridwen became a hawk on the wing, and the chase went on.

Gwion Bach became a grain of wheat on the threshing room floor. But Cerridwen became a black hen, and she pecked about on the floor until she found the single grain that was Gwion Bach, and when she had him she swallowed him whole.

Now if what is true is no lie, that grain of wheat lay in the belly of Cerridwen for the length of nine months, and after the passing of nine months, she gave birth to a baby boy. And although the boy was of sweet disposition and great beauty, she could not love him, so she bound him up in a leather bag and cast him into the sea.

The leather bag floated away on the waves and came and went with the swell of the tide from one season to the next and more, with the baby inside growing in age not one day older. Thus the ocean cradled the baby, safe on the rising and falling of her bosom, until the time came for him to be found. On May Eve, the waves carried the bag to the shores of the kingdom of Gwaelod, and there deposited it in the nets of King Gwyddno Garanhir who ruled that land.

It was the king's custom, every May Eve, to bestow the salmon fishing rights on some person he wished to favour, who could then claim the valuable catch that always lay in the nets at this time, in the weir near the shore between Divi and Aberystwyth. This year, the king had decided to grant the rights to his son Elphin, a hapless young man who seemed fated always to ill luck, in the hope that some good fortune might come of it.

Accordingly, on this particular May Eve, Elphin went down to the weir to see what bounty the nets might yield. To his dismay, however, he saw that they contained nothing but a battered old leather bag, disgorged by the sea. Cursing his misfortune, Elphin

nevertheless opened the bag – and there saw the fairest infant he had ever set eyes on, with such a radiant face that he cried out, *tâl iesin*, which means 'shining brow'. And so the child received its name: it was called Taliesin.

Elphin placed the infant Taliesin on the

CRACKS IN THE WHEEL OF TIME

It is no coincidence that Taliesin was delivered from Gwyddno's nets on May Eve – the eve of May Day – for this is a highly significant date in the Celtic calendar. It is the festival of Beltane, that ushers in Samradh, the summer half of the year that lasts until Halloween, or Samhain. Such borderline moments, when existence stands poised between one state and another, produce a 'crack' in the wheel of time when the normal rules that govern the physical world are temporarily suspended – a fissure in reality through which the Otherworld can gain access to the realm of mortals. Like Samhain, Beltane is therefore a time of weird, of great fatefulness and magic. It was at Beltane, for example, that the Tuatha Dé Danann, the gods of the Irish Celts and ancestors of the faery folk, arrived in Ireland in their chariots of cloud.

A PEOPLE OF THE NIGHT

The discovery of Taliesin on what the modern calendar deems May Eve, rather than May Day, relates to the way in which the Celts are believed to have counted time. For them, a day began not at midnight, but at dusk on the previous day. Hence, May Eve was seen as the beginning of Beltane. It was this method of calculating days that lead the Romans to refer to the Celts of Gaul as 'a people of the night'.

A YEAR AND A DAY

The practice of dividing time according to nightfall and the patterns of the moon is echoed in the 'year and a day' for which the Cauldron was set to boil. Familiar to us from many a fairy tale, this apparently fanciful phrase in fact refers to a lunar division of the year. Divide a year of 365 days by the 28-day lunar cycle, and this gives 13 'moons' with one day over.

BELOW: BELTANE (MAY EVE) WAS THE TIME OF TALIESIN'S 'SECOND BIRTH'. THIS, ALONG WITH ITS OPPOSITE, SAMHAIN, DIVIDED THE DARK HALF OF THE CELTIC YEAR FROM THE LIGHT HALF.

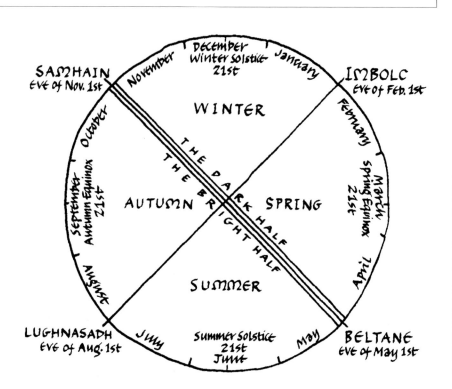

saddle behind him, and slowly rode home. Despondent at having come away with not a single salmon when others before him had found the nets bursting with fish, he felt his sorrow give way to amazement as he heard the child singing from behind him a song of poetry and consolation, telling Elphin that this was the luckiest day of his life, and that he, Taliesin, would be of greater service to him than three hundred salmon.

Elphin hurried to his father's castle and brought Taliesin before the king, announcing that he had caught something far finer than salmon – he had caught a child wonder, an infant bard. When the king asked Taliesin who he was and where he had come from, it was with these Words of Power that Taliesin replied:

> *'I come from the land of the summer stars.*
> *I have been with Noah on the Flood*
> *and I will sing my song till the*
> *world's end.*
> *I have been a salmon in the net,*
> *a fish in the water, a hare in the field,*
> *a dove in the air.*
> *I have been an eagle, a bull, a stallion,*
> *a snake,*
> *an axe and a sword.*
> *I have been the string on the harp of*
> *the bard.*
> *I have been the foam of the sea*
> *and the drop in a shower of rain.*
> *I have been a grain of wheat that grew*
> *on a hill.*
> *Three times have I been born.*
> *I am called Taliesin.'*

Never had such words of wonder sprung from the mouth of one so young, and the king and all his court marvelled.

Taliesin was brought up by Elphin and his wife, and he brought Elphin nothing but prosperity and good fortune from the day he entered his home. Later, when still only thirteen years old, he freed Elphin from imprisonment by his uncle Maelgan, confounding Maelgan's bards with a riddle, raising a storm wind that would bring the castle walls down, and dissolving Elphin's chains with a song.

ABOVE: CARDIGAN BAY WHERE, AT ABERYSTWYTH, TALIESIN WAS CAUGHT IN THE NETS OF KING GWYDDNO. IT WAS UNDER HIS RULE THAT THE LAND NOW BENEATH THE BAY WAS SAID TO HAVE BEEN LOST TO THE SEA, A DISASTER WHICH CAUSED THE KING TO SIGH HEAVILY – GIVING RISE TO THE PHRASE 'THE SIGH OF GWYDDNO' TO DESCRIBE A DEEP SIGH.

Born once as a boy who tasted the three Drops of Inspiration, grown once from a grain of wheat, and delivered once from out of the belly of the sea, thrice-born Taliesin of the Shining Brow may – if his words are to be believed – be with us still, in the rustling of the wind-blown leaves, in the call of the stag and the eagle, in the rush of the waves on the shore, or in any other form his eternal presence chooses to inhabit.

Classical Greece is the culture of origin of this tale, which serves to explain the weaving habits of the spider and also gives us the scientific name for this class of invertebrates. Associated with the Roman goddess Minerva, the Greek Athene of this story was not only the Goddess of Weaving but of Wisdom, too, a highly significant attribute here since the various 'spider' goddesses of different mythologies are the mistresses of fate who spin, measure and cut the Thread of Destiny.

THE SPIDER THAT SPINS

In a village by the shores of the Aegean Sea, there once lived a girl called Arachne. She was of a humble family; while her mother tended their few crops, her father would sail out onto the sea in his small, wooden boat, to catch fish.

But Arachne cared nothing for such mundane tasks, for she had a magical skill. Every morning, after her parents had left for their daily work, she would take up her place by her spinning wheel and there she would spin and spin, drawing out threads as fine as the hairs on a butterfly's wing, as light as thistledown on the breeze. The cloths she wove from these threads were soft as the mist that rises from the sea, and they sparkled in the light like all the stars of heaven.

News of Arachne's extraordinary skills began to spread, and the village girl was soon famous. Now she added splashes of colour to her cloths. One of these was a rich red-purple, of a rainbow brightness that had never been

seen before. The dye was obtained from shellfish that her fisherman father had brought home. The colour was to become the emblem of royalty, and was called Tyrian purple.

People came from all over the land to marvel at Arachne's work. As her wheel whirred and her loom clattered, her ears were filled with whisperings of wonder and praise and flattery.

The whisperings turned Arachne's head. She began to feel proud. She began to believe that she was the finest spinner and weaver in all the world, even greater than Athene herself, Goddess of Weaving and Wisdom and War – and she said as much, to anyone who cared to

ABOVE: THE GODDESS PALLAS ATHENE IN A PAINTING BY GUSTAV KLIMT (1862–1918). ASSOCIATED WITH WEAVING, WISDOM AND WAR – SHE IS A TRUE FATE GODDESS.

listen. She even went so far as to challenge the goddess to a weaving contest.

One day, among the small crowd gathered to watch Arachne at work, an old woman appeared. Her back was bent, she leant on a stick, and she was shrouded in a tattered, grey cloak. In a voice as old and broken as her body, she addressed Arachne. She reproved her for her impudence in challenging Athene, and advised her to ask for forgiveness. But Arachne refused to listen. She merely repeated her challenge, even more loudly than before.

As the old woman heard Arachne's words, a dramatic change came over her. Her cloak fell to the ground, her stick became a lance, and there – tall and straight and bearing her snake-headed shield on her arm – stood none other than shining-eyed Athene herself.

Even in the presence of the goddess herself, Arachne would not take back her boastful words. Two looms were brought, one for Athene, one for Arachne. On her loom, Athene wove pictures of the follies of mortals who believed they were greater than the gods, and who had been punished for their pride. On her loom, Arachne wove pictures of the follies of the gods. There was Zeus, Athene's father,

disguised as a cloud and enamoured of a white cow – once the priestess Io; there was Apollo, embracing a tree – once the nymph Daphne; there was Pan, serenading a reed – once the nymph Syrinx.

When Athene saw what the impudent Arachne had woven into her tapestry, she became very angry indeed. She raised her shuttle, touched Arachne on the forehead, and Arachne vanished. All that could be seen, beneath the stool on which the girl had been sitting, was a tiny black creature, with a round body and eight legs, that scuttled away into a crack in the wall.

Thus Arachne the Spinner became the Arachne the Spider, doomed to spin and weave for ever with the thread that she draws from her own body. To this day, we still remember her for she has given her name to her many descendants – they are all the species of spider that we know as the 'arachnids'.

BELOW: WATCHED BY ATHENE, ARACHNE WEAVES HER FATEFUL TAPESTRY IN A PAINTING BY TINTORETTO (1518–1594).

Like the story on page 56, this is another Maori tale which
focuses on the nocturnal habits of fairies. As usual, if they are
betrayed, they leave the human realm, never to return.

THE SECRET OF WEAVING

Once, long, long ago, people did not know how to weave or make baskets, for these were magical skills, belonging only to fairy women. But a day came when people stole the fairies' secret, and I will tell you how it all came about.

On a certain day, a man by the name of Karanga-roa went down to the sea and there he met a beautiful woman who had come to gather *rehia*, an edible seaweed. She was sitting on the rocks, sunning herself, and drying the *rehia* that she had picked. Karanga-roa sat

down beside her and the two fell into conversation. Karanga-roa very much liked the look of this lovely woman, and decided she would make a good wife, so you can imagine his delight when he asked her to marry him and she agreed.

Because she had come to gather *rehia*, Karanga-roa named his new wife Hine-rehia, and it was not long before she made him the proud father of a growing family.

Now Hine-rehia was a model wife in every way, but in one thing she excelled above all the other women of the village: she knew how to weave. As you have probably guessed, Hine-rehia was one of the fairy people. Every night, when all her family were fast asleep, she rose from her bed and set to work. First she would scrape the leaves of the flax with a shell, then she would wash and dry them, and from them would form the yarn for the weft. To make the yarn for the warp, she would twist a handful of fibres and beat them well with a stone, then she would roll them together on her thigh. And when the two yarns were dyed and ready, she would weave them together on her loom, that

Left: Maori women weaving flax. Because of the special, almost sacred nature of their craft, weavers had to observe *tapu* restrictions in preparing materials and executing the work.

gave out its soft clickety-clack into the stillness of the night.

Hine-rehia was also an excellent basket-maker, and would plait together strips of flax to make beautiful baskets and mats, into which she worked intricate patterns. But, as always, she would only do her weaving and plaiting at night, or on foggy days – never when it was bright and sunny – for, as she told her husband, 'The sun will steal my power.'

Now when the other women of the village saw the wonderful new clothes that Karanga-roa and his family were wearing – not to mention the gorgeous mats and baskets that now filled their house to overflowing – they were amazed for they had never set eyes on such wonders before … and, of course, they were jealous, too.

'How does she do it …' they whispered to each other, '…and anyway why should she be allowed to keep the secret to herself?'

Well, their envy and curiosity got the better of them, and they went to a *tohunga*, a magician, and persuaded him to bewitch Hine-rehia and confuse her into thinking it was still night when it was day. That way, they would have enough light to see by, and they could spy on her and discover exactly what she was getting up to. So the *tohunga* cast his spell and, suspecting nothing, Hine-rehia continued weaving and plaiting until the sun was high in the sky, and all the while, the women, safely concealed in their hiding place, were able to note all her techniques and secret skills.

But at last, the spell wore off, fatigue overcame Hine-rehia, and she laid her work down. She yawned and stretched and looked outside and saw – to her horror – that it was broad daylight, and she knew she had been tricked. So she placed herself beneath the smoke-hole in the centre of the roof, and sang a song of farewell. Then a cloud came down through the roof and carried her back to her home in the mountains, and she was never seen again.

But sometimes at night or when it is very foggy, her song may still be heard on the rooftops, and then people know that a death will shortly follow.

And if anything is to be learned from this

ABOVE: LIKE OTHER FAIRY-WOMEN, HINE-REHIA'S HOME WAS IN THE MOUNTAINS. IN MAORI BELIEF, MOUNTAINS WERE PLACES OF GREAT SACREDNESS, THE ABODE OF SPIRITS AND THE BURIAL PLACE OF IMPORTANT ANCESTORS.

sad tale, it is this: fairies must work by night and women must work by day … and let that be a lesson to us all.

FAIRY GODMOTHERS

In Northern European tradition, there is also a strong connection between spinning and weaving and certain fairy women. Such fairies were, in fact, the Fates thinly disguised – the word 'fairy' is itself etymologically connected with 'fate', through 'fey', 'fata' (Latin for 'fate') and 'fatare' (Latin for 'enchant') – and their spinning wheels were the wheels of fortune. Probably the most famous was the old spinner-woman in the tower in 'The Sleeping Beauty', who just 'happened' to be discovered by the princess on her fifteenth birthday. This crone was, of course, the thirteenth Wise Woman, come to implement her prophesy made at the princess's christening. Echoes of the spinning goddess may also be found in the figure of Mother Holle in the Grimms' collection and in every fairy godmother who appears to determine a heroine's fortunes.

THE BANSHEE

The crying of the lost fairy wife that foretells death in this story recalls the activities of the Irish banshee, or 'beansídhe', the fairy woman of the mounds ('sídhe' is Gaelic for hill, or burial mound). When her wailing is heard, a death will surely follow.

VEGETATION &
FERTILITY

Dependent on nature for its survival, mankind has
always seen the annual renewal of fertility as a
cause for celebration. In ancient times, certain
crops were so important to this survival that they
were personified as deities, whose cyclical pattern
of death and rebirth was enshrined in myth.

CHAPTER FIVE

This Babylonian myth explains the changing of the seasons. The narrative focuses on Tammuz who was a god of vegetation, particularly of the corn, and the lover of the goddess Ishtar. His death is an obvious analogy for the corn harvest. The earlier Sumerian counterparts of Ishtar and Tammuz were Inanna and her lover Dumuzi.

ISHTAR AND TAMMUZ

Tammuz was the beloved of Ishtar, Queen of Heaven, and he was beautiful. In the fields of corn that slowly turned from green to gold as spring passed into summer they would be seen walking together. But a terrible day was to come when Ishtar would lose her lover, and would have to travel to the ends of the earth,

and endure much pain and suffering, in order to bring him back.

It all began in the month that bears his name, in the burning days of late summer, for it was then that the people came to the fields where Tammuz stood, and cruelly murdered him, hacking him to death with their sickles, scattering his flesh over the land until it ran red with his blood, grinding his bones to powder and scattering it to the winds, like flour blown from the miller's stone.

When the goddess learned of the death of her beloved, she was distraught with grief. Standing like the shining cedar, straight and proud and tall, she lifted her voice in a loud

LEFT: ISHTAR STANDS ON A MOUNTAINTOP WITH TWO OF HER PRIESTESSES. THIS SCULPTURE, DATING FROM THE TIME OF THE AMORITE DYNASTIES OF THE 19TH AND 18TH CENTURIES BC, WAS FOUND AT MARI, TODAY TALL-AL-HARIRI IN SYRIA.

where no cypresses grow. She sang for the garden that has neither vine nor hive. She sang for the meadow where no wildflowers bloom.

Weary and worn from weeping, the goddess knew that she must find the spirit of Tammuz and attempt to bring him back to life, whatever the perils that faced her. She knew just where to look. He would be in gloomy Irkalla, the House of Darkness, where dust lies on door and bolt, and from which there is no returning. He would be with the *edimmu*, the souls of the dead, both the mighty and the humble, who are clad, like birds, in garments of wings, whose existence is lighted only by the dimness of dusk, whose only food is mud. In Irkalla Ishtar would find Tammuz, so it was to Irkalla that she went.

Now it so happened that the ruler of this land of no return was none other than Ishtar's own sister. Her name was Erishkigal, and

lament that echoed through all of heaven and earth. She called out for her Tammuz, her child and her enchanter, and in her sorrow she grieved for all the barren and empty places that were bereft of life as her world was now bereft of Tammuz.

She sang for the great river where no willows grow. She sang for the field where neither wheat nor barley nor herbs spring. She sang for the ear of corn that is empty of its seed. She sang for the pool where no fishes swim. She sang for the thicket where no reeds flourish. She sang for the wood where no tamarisks rise. She sang for the wilderness

BELOW: TWO DEITIES STAND IN SUPPLICATION BEFORE ISHTAR IN HER ROLE AS WAR GODDESS, IN THIS SEAL IMPRESSION DATING FROM THE FIRST AMORITE DYNASTY (1830–1350 BC).

Meanwhile back on earth and in heaven, all mourned the loss of Ishtar, and all grieved sore, for without the goddess's influence, nothing was able to thrive. The bull refused to cover the cow; the ass no longer approached the she-ass; and in the city street, the man no longer called after the maidservant. The world was thrown into such desolation that at last Sîn, God of the Moon, and Shamash, God of the Sun, appealed to Ea, Lord of Magic and Master of the Waters that nourish the earth and contain all wisdom. And Ea created a messenger, Asushu-Namir, and sent him to Irkalla, to the land of no return, with magic words to overcome the will of Erishkigal.

And even though her own powers were great, and she tried to bind the messenger with

when she heard that Ishtar was making a journey to see her, she feared that her sister wished to seize her throne, so she devised a plan to rob Ishtar of her divine power. The goddess might be allowed admittance, Erishkigal said, but as she passed each of the entrance gates of hell she must disrobe until in the end she came before Erishkigal naked. Without her vestments of power, Erishkigal knew, Ishtar would be helpless.

Ishtar was forced to agree, and so, at each of the seven gates of Irkalla, she removed one garment or one adornment: first the crown from her head; then the pendants from her ears; then the necklace from her throat; then the jewels from her breast; then the girdle from her waist; then the bracelets from her wrists and ankles; and, last, the very gown that covered her. Thus, naked as a newborn babe, Ishtar presented herself before the throne of Erishkigal.

But Erishkigal still did not trust her and made her a prisoner and inflicted on her terrible torments, finally impaling her on a stake.

RIGHT: IN HER QUEST FOR TAMMUZ, ISHTAR, STRIPPED OF HER GARMENTS AND HER DIVINE POWER, STANDS BEFORE THE THRONE OF THE RULER OF THE UNDERWORLD.

a great spell, Erishkigal could not resist the magic of Ea and was forced to release Ishtar. And when the body of Ishtar was sprinkled with the water of life, she awoke as if from a deep sleep, and all her bruises and the marks of her wounds vanished. Passing back through the seven gates of hell, Ishtar replaced each of the garments or adornments that she had hitherto removed, and with each piece of attire her vigour was restored once, twice, three times, until in the end her bloom and her beauty and her power was returned to her sevenfold.

It was further agreed that Tammuz, who all this time had been languishing in Irkalla, should return to the land of the living – but, Erishkigal demanded, there was one condition. Tammuz might spend one half of the year in freedom; for the other half he must return to live with her.

And that is how Tammuz came to be shared between the two sisters, one the Queen of Heaven, the other the Queen of Hell. When Tammuz was with Ishtar on the earth, the goddess rejoiced and nature and man flourished. But when he returned to Erishkigal below, Ishtar grieved and all signs of life died.

This is how it has been from the beginning of time, and this is how it will be to the end.

ADONIS

The Syrian vegetation deity Adonis was one of several incarnations of the Sumerian Dumuzi and Babylonian Tammuz. Adonis was paired with the goddess Astarte – the 'Lady of Byblos' and equivalent of Ishtar – and later, in Greek myth, of their counterpart Aphrodite. His name originally simply meant 'lord', from the Semitic Adon, and would have been merely a title of honour by which worshippers addressed Tammuz, in the same way as the Hebrew god Yahweh is referred to as Adonai in the Bible. Gored to death by a boar while hunting, Adonis' gushing blood coloured the red anemone, which became his flower. His death and resurrection were the cause of an eight-day celebration known as the Adonia, held in Syria, Judea, Egypt, Persia, Cyprus and Greece.

ATTIS

Phrygian Attis, another vegetation deity and sacrificial god from western Anatolia, was the beloved of the goddess Cybele, whose worship was transported to Rome in 204 BC. Son of the Virgin Mother Nana, who conceived him by eating an almond or pomegranate, he was either killed by a boar, like Adonis, or castrated himself, like the priests of Cybele, under a pine tree, into which he subsequently metamorphosed. Violets sprang from his blood. His death and resurrection were celebrated from 22–25 March, close to the modern Easter.

This famous myth features two major figures of the Egyptian pantheon, the goddess Isis and her brother-husband Osiris. The story is an analogy for the inundatation of the Nile that ends the drought of high summer, and is so crucial to the production of crops and hence the survival of the people. The resurrected Osiris, who personifies the flood and is the agent of the land's fertility, therefore fulfils the role of a saviour god.

ISIS AND OSIRIS

There was once a good and wise king by the name of Osiris who ruled the land of Egypt. Before he took the throne, the people had been wild and barbarous, but Osiris brought order to their ways by giving them a set of laws to follow; he also taught them the skills of husbandry – how to till the soil, how to sow the seed, how to grow and harvest the corn and the vine – and under the influence of his benign kingship, the land and the people flourished and prospered.

The wife of Osiris was Queen Isis, and when Osiris was away imparting his wisdom to other races, she ruled in his stead. Osiris was loved by all – except for one, that is, who was of his own flesh and blood. This was his brother Set – red-haired Set whose locks were as fiery as the scorching desert that surrounded the rich, black plains of the Nile and threatened always to consume them. In his hard heart, Set nourished a hatred for his brother Osiris, and wished in any way he could to do him harm.

So it was that one day Set met with Aso, Queen of Ethiopia, and seventy-two others, and conspiring together they hatched a plot to bring about the downfall of Osiris. By secret means, Set ascertained the exact height and shape of his brother, and ordered a magnificent coffin to be made, adorned with carvings and pictures as were suitable for a receptacle for the dead. Then he invited the unsuspecting Osiris to a lavish feast.

When all had eaten and drunk their fill, Set proposed a game.

'Come, my friends,' said he. 'See here this beautiful casket … let us try a little experiment – let us each try it for size, as if it were a shoe, and see which one of us it fits …'

One by one, the company stepped into the coffin and lay down in it, but some were too tall, some too short, some too fat, some too thin – it fitted none of them. And then Osiris, unaware that he was being led straight into a trap, lay down in it and the coffin fitted him like a glove, following every curve, every line of his body, as if it been moulded around him.

'Dearest brother!' exclaimed Set in mock amazement. 'It could have been made for you!'

And so saying, he and his accomplices rushed toward the coffin, slammed down the lid, nailed it in place, and poured molten lead on it to seal up every opening. Then he ordered the chest to be carried to the Nile and set to float on the waters.

Entombed in this vessel of death, Osiris was helpless. He could not move in the confined space it allowed, and what was the point of screaming when there was no one there to hear? Without air, without light, without water, without food, Osiris felt the life force slowly ebbing from him, like blood oozing from a wound, and he died.

Carried by the river current, the coffin continued its slow voyage down the Nile, out through its mouth into the blue waters of the Mediterranean, and across the sea where, after days or months, it was cast ashore at Byblos on

ABOVE: IN THIS DETAIL FROM AN EGYPTIAN COFFIN FROM THE 1ST CENTURY BC, THE BODY OF OSIRIS LIES ON ITS FUNERARY BIER. THE FALCON OR HAWK HOVERING ABOVE HIM IS ISIS TRANSFORMED, FANNING LIFE INTO HIM WITH HER WINGS.

the coast of Syria, and came to rest at the foot of a tamarisk tree. And there the body of Osiris lay, unheeded, uncared-for and untended. But the tree, like a mother enfolding her child, began to wrap around the coffin fingers of bark and to take Osiris into its bosom, until in the end a mighty trunk surrounded him and above his head magnificent branches sprang. Indeed, so wondrous was the tamarisk tree that news of it spread and when the king of that land, Melcanthus by name, heard tell of it and came to see it for himself, so impressed was he by its size and splendour that he ordered it to be cut down and made into a pillar that would support the roof of his palace. This was done, but little did the king suspect what the pillar really contained, deep in the heart of its woody core.

Meanwhile, back in Egypt, Isis had discovered the cruel murder of her husband and was distraught with grief. So she cut a lock from her hair and dressed herself in the garments of mourning and set off into the wide, wide world to seek the body of her loved one and bring it home, and everywhere she went, she asked, 'Have you seen the coffin of Osiris?' but the answer was always no.

Then one day, her luck changed. While talking to some children whose custom it was to play by the riverside, she learnt that they had seen just such a casket as that containing Osiris drifting along the Nile, towards its mouth. Using her divinatory powers to delve deeper, she discovered that the coffin of Osiris had crossed the sea, had been taken into the bosom of a tree, and that the trunk of that tree now supported the roof of the palace of Melcanthus in Byblos. Without further ado, that is where she went.

Arrived in Byblos, she set herself by the side of a spring and waited, and it wasn't long before the handmaidens of Queen Astarte arrived to cool themselves by the water. Without giving away her identity, Isis struck up a conversation with them and, as they talked, she plaited their hair and caressed their skin and their clothes with her fragrant breath that was like a sweet breeze that carries all the perfumes of a garden.

When the handmaidens returned to the palace, the queen asked why their hair and skin and clothes were so beautifully perfumed, and they told her about the stranger at the spring. Astarte summoned Isis, greeted her, and asked her to become the nurse to one of the young princes.

At last Isis was inside the palace, where the body of her beloved Osiris lay hidden. Nevertheless, she did not neglect her duties as a nurse. Every night she fed the young prince by allowing him to suck on her finger, and every night she placed his body in the fire to purify him and prepare him to receive her gift

of immortality. And every night, too, she would assume her other form – that of the swallow – and would sing a song of sadness for her dead husband.

Now, even in the spaciousness of a palace, such goings-on cannot go unnoticed indefinitely, and it was not long before news of Isis' nocturnal habits reached the ears of the queen, who resolved to observe for herself just what was going on – and when, from her hiding place, she saw Isis prepare to plunge her son into the flames, she did what any mother would do … she screamed, rushed out and angrily snatched the child from the nurse's clutches. Then Isis was forced to reveal her true identity and the purpose of her mission. Her wish to cut open the tamarisk pillar was granted, and when she saw the coffin of Osiris she began to wail, and her wailing was like the wind that moans over the desert, and it so terrified one of the young sons of Astarte that he died of fright.

Isis set sail with the coffin for Egypt and during the voyage she transformed herself into a kite and hovered over the body of Osiris, fanning it with the beating of her wings, and in this form she conceived a son by him, whose name would be Horus. Once in Egypt, she secreted the coffin in the marshes of the Nile delta and went to Buto, there to attend to her young son.

Now it so happened that, while Isis was thus occupied, Set, who was out hunting wild boar by the light of the full moon, came upon a coffin hidden in the reeds of the marsh – the very coffin in which he had entombed his brother Osiris! He recognized it at once. Enraged, he ripped off the lid, hauled out the body, and cut it into fourteen pieces, which he scattered to the winds.

When Isis returned and found the coffin empty, she began her search once again, sailing through the swamps in a papyrus boat. Aided by her sister Nephthys, the gods Thoth and Anubis, and her son Horus, she at last found all the fragments of the body, save one, the phallus, which had been eaten by a crab. She fashioned an exact replica and then cunningly reassembled all the parts to make one whole. The sacred embalming rites were then performed and Osiris wrapped in the bandages of a mummy, whereupon Isis once again fanned him with her wings and blew back into him the spirit of life, so that he was revived and took his place in the underworld as Ruler of Eternity.

But Osiris did not stay in the underworld for ever, and to this day his returning presence may still be detected at certain seasons in Egypt, as can the spirits of Set and Isis, too, for those with eyes that know how to see. Set you will find in the burning, life-denying desert; Osiris you will see in the the revived Nile that inundates the scorched fields after summer's drought, making them fertile and causing the dormant corn to rise; Isis is there in the land itself, in the soft, sweet wind that whispers over the sleeping seeds like a fluttering bird breathing into them the breath of life, and in the dog star Sirius whose joyous rise heralds the coming flood. And to that flood Isis adds her own, for as the Nile begins to swell, the rising waters are said to be the tears of Isis as she cries Osiris back to life.

ABOVE: ISIS SUCKLES THE INFANT HORUS – OSIRIS REINCARNATED IN HIS SON. HORUS WOULD LATER AVENGE HIS FATHER'S MURDER BY KILLING SET, WHO REPRESENTED THE BARREN HALF OF THE YEAR.

In this very well-known myth from classical Greece, winter is explained as the time when the Earth Mother Demeter, the source of fertility, goes into mourning for her daughter, the spirit of spring, who has temporarily been taken from the world. The Demeter and Persephone of the Greek story were known in Rome as Ceres and Proserpine respectively. Ceres, the Roman Goddess of Agriculture, gives us our word 'cereal'. Some details in this myth exactly parallel those in the tale on pages 116–119.

HOW WINTER CAME INTO THE WORLD

Long, long ago, when the memory of man was new, mortals lived in an endless summer. There was neither cold nor snow nor ice, but sun-gold days and balmy nights, fruitfulness and plenty. But then, one dark day, a great misfortune befell the daughter of Demeter, and it was this that first brought winter to the world.

ABOVE: WITH A THUNDERING OF HOOVES AND A RUMBLING OF CHARIOT WHEELS, HADES CARRIES OFF THE DAUGHTER OF DEMETER, IN A PAINTING BY JOSEPH HEINTZ (1564–1609).

Demeter was goddess of the fertile land, and her hair was the colour of ripened corn. The name of her daughter was Kore, a maiden as fresh and fair as the blossom that bursts on the trees in spring.

One day, Kore was out in the meadows gathering flowers with her companions – violets, hyacinths, irises, lilies – when she noticed a narcissus of particular beauty, and stooped to pick it. As she did so, it was as if she had turned a key and opened the way to some dark subterranean chamber, for no sooner had she plucked the bloom than a deep rumbling was heard from below, and the birds stopped singing, and the earth began to shake and shiver. Kore screamed as a huge chasm appeared before her, and out of it thundered Hades, Lord of the Underworld, in his chariot. Before she had a chance to cry out for help, Hades had seized her and carried her away with him to his kingdom. And when they had gone, the wound in the earth closed over and all was as peaceful as before, with no sign that anything had ever been amiss.

When Demeter heard of the disappearance of her daughter, it was as if all light and life had gone out of the world. Flinging over her shoulder the sombre veil of sorrow, the goddess flew like a bird over land and sea, seeking for her lost child. When at last she discovered the name of the thief – and worse still, that Zeus, Lord of the gods and brother to Hades, had conspired in the crime – she was beyond herself with rage and despair. She disguised herself as an old woman, and desolately wandered the world of man looking for her daughter.

At last she came to Eleusis, that was ruled by the wise king Celeus. No one guessed her true identity, and in the king's palace she bided her time, becoming nurse to his infant son. It was the goddess's secret plan to confer on the boy the gift of immortality and so, instead of food, she breathed on him and anointed him with divine ambrosia and placed him in the coals of the fire at night to burn away his mortality, and every day the child became more like a god.

Anxious to discover the reason for the change in her son, the boy's mother Metaneira spied on Demeter, little guessing who this nurse truly was. When she saw her lowering the boy into the fire, she screamed, whereupon the goddess turned and told her that, had it not been for her interference, her son would have become immortal. Then Demeter revealed her true identity, and commanded that a temple be built for her in Eleusis, where the people might come to celebrate her mysteries.

In gratitude to Celeus' family for their hospitality, she also imparted to their son, Triptolemus, her secrets. It was to Triptolemus that she gave the first grain of corn, and taught him how to sow it that it might bring forth rich harvests and feed mankind. It was to Triptolemus that she showed the way to harness oxen to the plough to aid the farmer in his daily work. It was to Triptolemus that she gave a winged chariot drawn by dragons so that he might travel the world spreading the knowledge she had taught him among all men.

But all that is a story for another day, for now we must continue with the goddess in her quest. Seated in her temple at Eleusis, Demeter vowed revenge for the theft of her daughter, and it was a terrible revenge indeed, for the goddess placed a curse on the land, saying that it would not bear any fruit until Kore was

BELOW: THE MOURNING OF DEMETER FOR HER ABDUCTED DAUGHTER, SHOWN HERE IN A PAINTING BY EVELYN DE MORGAN (1855–1919), WAS AN ALLEGORY FOR THE BARRENNESS OF WINTER, WHEN NATURE REFUSES TO FLOURISH.

returned to her. And so it was. For the first time since man and beast had walked the earth, the corn would not grow, the fruit would not ripen, and cold and darkness, famine and death spread a black cloak over the world. Every creature, every mortal was afflicted with a terrible and biting hunger.

In desperation, Zeus sent Iris to plead with the goddess. Descending to earth on her rainbow bridge, Iris begged Demeter to relent, but it was of no use. One by one, the gods came, but still the goddess was obdurate, still she refused to listen, still the land lay barren. At last, the only solution was for Zeus himself to speak to his brother Hades and command him to return Kore to her mother.

Hades agreed readily enough, too readily, it must be said. The truth is that Hades had known all along that this moment would come so he had prepared himself for it – he had laid a little trap for Kore to ensure that she would not be able to desert him totally. While she was in his kingdom, he had offered her a pomegranate, the 'apple with many seeds'. Only four of the seeds had passed the unsuspecting maiden's lips, but this was enough to seal her fate, for the magical pomegranate is the fruit of sexual union. Swallowing even part of it bound Kore to Hades in the sacred ties of marriage. She was now his wife, and had a new name: she had become Persephone, Queen of the Underworld.

And that is why, when Zeus told Hades to release his wife, he was not too reluctant to do so, for he knew that she would soon be back.

BELOW: AN ANCIENT GREEK RELIEF SHOWING PERSEPHONE, DEMETER AND TRIPTOLEMUS, TO WHOM DEMETER TAUGHT THE ARTS OF AGRICULTURE. TRIPTOLEMUS WAS ALSO KNOWN AS 'THREE PLOUGHINGS', REFERRING TO THE BELIEF THAT HE HAD LAIN THREE TIMES WITH THE EARTH MOTHER DEMETER.

FORBIDDEN FRUIT

In folklore generally, ingesting any food or drink offered during a sojourn in the Otherworld is likely to lead to trouble. Usually, one falls under supernatural possession of some kind and enters an altered state – one may forget one's former life entirely and be lost to friends and family, or one may forfeit the power to leave voluntarily. Conversely, ingesting forbidden fruit or drink may confer immortality.

FRUITS OF FERTILITY

In the ancient world, the pomegranate, the fig and the apricot were all considered symbols of fertility, and of female sexuality – fig trees were a favourite resting spot for satyrs, known for their lustful appetites. Beans were also an ancient symbol of female fertility. In a Twelfth Night tradition, the title 'King of the Bean' was conferred on the man who found a bean in his plum cake, representing union with the female.

As his queen, she would have to return, to spend four months of each year with him in his kingdom in the Underworld – one month for every seed swallowed.

And that is why, for four months every year, Demeter goes into mourning for her daughter, and the leaves fall from the trees and the land is bare and all the world sleeps, waiting for the return of Kore.

ABOVE: IN THIS CHRISTIANIZED VIEW OF THE GREEK AFTERWORLD, AN AGEING PERSEPHONE SITS NEXT TO HADES. CERBERUS, THE UNDER-WORLD'S THREE-HEADED WATCHDOG RESTS BEFORE THEM, WHILE ON THE RIGHT SINNERS ENDURE THE TORTURES OF HELL.

This exquisite tale from the Ojibwe of the Great Lakes region of North America describes, in mythic imagery, the discovery of the cultivation of maize. It was recorded, among other legends, from oral tradition by Henry Rowe Schoolcraft, a United States government agent, in the 1820s. This particular tale became the basis of Hiawatha's Fasting in Henry Wadsworth Longfellow's famous narrative poem 'The Song of Hiawatha', published in 1855.

MONDAMIN AND THE INDIAN CORN

There was once a poor man who lived with his wife and children in a beautiful land of lakes and mountains and forests. To provide food for his family, the father would go out hunting, and his wife and those children who were old enough would gather berries and fruits from the bushes, and in this way they survived. But sometimes, when snow lay heavy on the ground and smothered the land in a blanket of silence, when the lakes were frozen into sheets of milky blue ice, there was no food to be had, and then the family would go hungry.

Now the man's eldest son was called Wunzh, and a day came when he had reached the age to undertake Ke-ig-nish-im-o-win, the fast to discover his spirit guide, the one who would be his guardian and lead him through life. And so, as was the custom, the father built a lodge, some way from where the family lived, where the youth might pass the solitary seven days of his trial, for this quest was not a

LEFT: WUNZH PROVIDED A MODEL FOR THE HERO HIAWATHA, SHOWN HERE IN A 1906 ILLUSTRATION BY HARRISON FISHER.

journey out into the world, but a journey into the land of the soul.

Accordingly, Wunzh took up his place in the lodge and began his fast. And on the first day of his fast, he went for a walk in the forest. Picking his way along a narrow path between the trees and the undergrowth, he was suddenly startled by a deer that shot out of a thicket just ahead of him, followed almost immediately by a rabbit that darted out of its burrow. Wunzh looked up at the tangle of branches above him, and there saw Adjidaumo the squirrel with his hoard of acorns, and higher up the nest of Omeme the pigeon, and higher even than that, in the little patches of blue caught between the branches like scraps of torn cloth, he caught sight of Wawa the wildgoose, flying across the roof of the forest towards the lake. And Wunzh was grateful for the forest's bounty, but remembered how lifeless it was in winter, and how hard it was then to find food, and he prayed to the Great Spirit:

'Master of Life, must it always be so?'

On the second day of his fast, Wunzh went for a walk in the meadows by the river. The West Wind was running lightly through the grass, the warm air hummed with the droning of insects, and on the bushes Wunzh could see Meenahga the blueberry and Shahbomin the gooseberry, and beneath them the stems and leaves and fruit of Odahmin the wild strawberry. Closer to the river, where the alder trees grew, he saw Bemahgut the wild vine, and pushing its way up out of the damp earth Mahnomonee the wild rice. And Wunzh was grateful for the meadow's bounty, but remembered how barren it was in winter, and how hard it was then to find food, and he prayed to the Great Spirit:

'Master of Life, must it always be so?'

On the third day of his fast, Wunzh went for a walk by the lake. The water was still and reflected the sky like a giant's mirror. Suddenly, with a plash and a plop, Nahma the sturgeon broke the surface, and Wunzh looked down into the translucent water and saw the yellow flash of Sahwa the perch. There, too, was Okahahwis the herring and, with his deadly jaws, Maskenozha the pike. And Wunzh was

grateful for the lake's bounty, but remembered how frozen it was in winter, and how hard it was then to find food, and he prayed to the Great Spirit:

'Master of Life, must it always be so?'

On the fourth day of his fast, Wunzh was too tired to go walking for no food had passed his lips for some time and he was growing weaker, so he stayed in his lodge and rested, and waited to see what he should see. All day he lay there, and his mind was visited by strange imaginings and hazy visions, that danced before him like flickering shadows from the fire, and he could not tell whether he was awake or dreaming, because of his faintness.

And as the day drew to its close, as the sun began to melt into the west coating mountains and lakes in liquid gold, as the purple mist of twilight drifted into every corner of Wunzh's vision, touching the world with magic, he thought he saw a figure coming towards him, out of the sky, out of the sunset. It was the figure of a man with golden hair, wearing a waving plume of silvery feathers and dressed in garments of green.

'The Master of Life has heard your prayers and has sent me to you,' said the stranger. 'But before your prayers can be answered, you must first wrestle with me.'

Somehow, although he was exhausted and faint with hunger, Wunzh felt a surge of courage rise up within him that gave him enough strength to stand and fight the stranger, and when they had wrestled for a time and Wunzh was almost defeated, the stranger said,

'That is enough for now. Tomorrow I will return to test you again,' and he disappeared by the same way he had come.

On the fifth day, everything happened as on the day before. Wunzh lay in his lodge, growing ever weaker, and as the sun set and twilight fell, the mysterious stranger appeared again to continue their fight. Again, Wunzh felt a surge of rising courage that gave him strength, and it was as if the weaker he grew in body, the stronger he became in heart. He wrestled with his mysterious opponent until he could hardly stand, whereupon the stranger called a halt as before, and promised to return the following day to test him again.

On the sixth day, it was the same. But this time, before the stranger departed, he turned to Wunzh and said:

'The Master of Life has seen the pureness of your heart. He sees that you do not wish for personal glory or riches but only to benefit others. Tomorrow is the last day of your trial; tomorrow you will vanquish me. When I am dead, strip off my garments and prepare the place where I have fallen and make sure that the earth there is soft and free of roots, then bury me there. Do not disturb my grave but visit it now and then and clear it of weeds and grass, and every month cover it with fresh earth. Do all of this, and you will have the answer to your prayers.'

And so saying, he disappeared, vanishing back into the sunset, into the sky.

On the seventh day, Wunzh's father came to the lodge with some food for him.

'My son,' he said, 'you have completed your trial with honour. Here, take … eat! The Master of Life does not want you to die.'

But weak as he was, Wunzh refused his father's kindness, for what he needed was not food for the body but food for the spirit. He knew he must hold on to his courage and continue his fast until sunset, when the stranger would visit him for the last time.

Sure enough, as the sun hid his face behind the mountaintop, and the soft veils of dusk drifted down, there was the stranger, just as he said he would be, with his golden hair and his waving plume of silvery feathers and his green

BELOW: 'DEAD HE LAY THERE IN THE SUNSET' – THE PROSTRATE FORM OF THE GREEN-PLUMED AND TASSELLED CORN SPIRIT MONDAMIN LIES BEFORE A VICTORIOUS HIAWATHA, IN AN ILLUSTRATION BY M. L. KIRK FROM 1910.

garments, and the pair set to in a ferocious struggle. As they battled and grappled and tussled, hair and feathers and fringes and mountains and sky and land reeled by in a whirlwind of shapes and colours, but in the end – Wunzh could hardly believe it – his opponent lay dead at his feet.

Wunzh stripped off the stranger's headdress and clothes, and buried his body in the earth, as he had been instructed to, and then he returned to his family, who were overjoyed to see him still alive. He told them nothing of his experience during his fast, but secretly went to visit the stranger's grave and tended it well. And the spring rains came and watered the spot where the stranger lay buried, and then spring ripened into summer and the hot sun shone down on the earth and called to everything, 'Grow, grow!' But still Wunzh said nothing of his experience during his fast.

Then one day, when summer was mellowing into autumn and all living things were satiated with the warmth of the sun, Wunzh lead his father to the quiet place when he had undertaken the fast of Ke-ig-nish-im-o-win, and there – on the grave of the stranger from the sky – stood a stately plant, with a tall stem and long green leaves and a plume of silvery tassels, and wrapped in a snug envelope of overlapping leaves was a fat corn cob, covered with sweet, juicy, yellow kernels.

'Do you see?' Wunzh said to his father. 'Do you see? This is my friend Mondamin – Mondamin the maize. From now on, we need never go hungry again … from now on, we can grow our own food. In the spring, we will plant the maize seeds and in the autumn we will harvest the crop and store it for the winter. This is the gift from the Master of Life – this is his gift to all of mankind.'

And Wunzh showed the people how to strip the cobs and how to sow the seeds in blocks so that the wind could blow the pollen in the tassels from one plant to the next to make them bear fruit. The people watched what he did and, in so doing, they learned how to grow their own food. And from that day on, they never went hungry again, for they had been given the divine gift of Indian Corn.

CORN GODS

The death and burial of the mysterious stranger from the sky in this story follows the typical pattern of the dying and resurrected god who personified the 'corn' – be it maize, wheat, barley, or any other grain – that provided a staple food for a particular people. The reaping of the corn symbolized the god's death, and the planting of the seed represented the burial of his body that would fertilize the earth and make it bear fruit. The god's death, therefore, was an absolute prerequisite for his rebirth, and this alternating pattern perfectly mirrored the endlessly repeating vegetative cycle of germination, growth, fruiting and decay.

OSIRIS

In ancient Egypt, wheat was identified with the god Osiris (see page 119). When his 'body' – the wheat that sprouted from his corpse and in which he was manifest – was harvested and made into cakes, it was eaten by his worshippers in holy sacrament in order to partake of his divinity, in much the same way as modern Christians observe the rite of Holy Communion. Thus a corn god could be a saviour in two senses: he not only provided salvation for the body by providing it with food, but he also offered salvation for the soul by allowing it communion with the divine.

DIONYSOS

In ancient Greece, the god Dionysos numbered, among his many attributes, associations with both the wheat and the vine (see page 128). Like Christ, the 'flesh' of Dionysos was eaten in the form of wheat cakes, and his 'blood' was drunk in the form of wine. One of his emblems was the winnowing basket, an item used for centuries to toss the grain in the air in order to separate the wheat from the chaff. At birth, the god is said to have been placed in a winnowing basket or 'liknon', hence his other name of Liknites. The 'liknon' is strongly reminiscent of the improvized cradle in which the saviour god of the Christians, Jesus Christ, was laid – the manger in the stable at Bethlehem.

In this famous nature story from classical Greece, the fates of two characters are intertwined, the behaviour of one affecting the destiny of the other. By means of anthropomorphosis, whereby animate and inanimate objects are given a human face, the tale also provides a clever explanation for the origins of the echo, and the growth habit and appearance of a familiar flower.

ECHO AND NARCISSUS

The world around us has not always been as we now believe it to be; once, it teemed with spirits that inhabited every place and every part of nature. There were spirits in the trees, in streams and rivers, in valleys and in mountains – all were imbued with a faery presence. The ancient Greeks had a name for these spirits. They called them nymphs. The nymphs of valley and wood were the Napaeae, the Auloniads, the Hylaeorae and the Alsaeids; the nymphs who lived in trees were the Dryads; and the nymphs who haunted mountain and grotto were the Oreads.

Such a one was Echo, an Oread in the retinue of the great goddess Hera. Now Hera had a problem, and that was her husband Zeus. Zeus simply loved women – tall ones, short ones, dark ones, fair ones, slim ones, plump ones. No woman was safe from him, be she mortal or immortal.

Zeus could never stay faithful to Hera for long, and Hera had her work cut out trying to keep an eye on her philandering husband – a task not helped by Echo who, whenever Zeus was whispering endearments and cooing sweet nothings to his latest favourite, would prattle and chatter and babble, thoroughly distracting Hera and preventing her from attending to her husband's activities. At last, exasperated by Echo's persistent talkativeness, the goddess

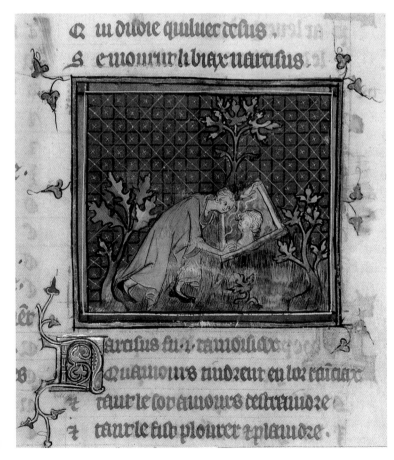

ABOVE: A SWOONING, LOVESTRUCK NARCISSUS
IS WATCHED BY A FADING ECHO, IN THIS
PAINTING BY NICHOLAS POUSSIN (1594–1665).

determined to put a stop to it once and for all.

'If you cannot stop talking,' said the angry Hera, 'then so be it. From now on, you will always have the last word.'

'… last word,' replied the startled Echo. And so it was, from that time on, that Echo could utter no words of her own, but was condemned only to repeat the last words spoken to her. In shame, she left the company of nymphs and went to hide herself in the caverns and hollows of the mountains.

Now it so happened that one day, when Echo was wandering her mountainside alone, she spied a handsome young man, out hunting. Instead of the thick black curls that most other men of the region had, this youth had golden-yellow hair as pale and bright as a spring morning, and Echo conceived an immediate passion for him.

'Who's there?' called out the young man, hearing Echo's faint footstep.

'… there?' replied Echo.

'What's your name?' asked the young man.

'… your name?' replied Echo.

With no words of her own to declare her love or even to announce her own name, Echo, sorrowful and broken-hearted, shrank back into the caves of the mountain, where she faded to nothing, until all that was left of her was her voice.

As for the young man, an equally strange fate befell him. Making his way down the mountain, he stopped to drink by a stream and there, looking down into the shining water, he saw his own face for the first time. He did not know to whom the face belonged, but it was of such surpassing beauty, framed by golden-yellow hair as pale and bright as a spring morning, that he fell in love with it on the spot. Narcissus – for that was the young man's name – had fallen in love with his own reflection.

Forgetting all else but the beautiful face gazing back at him, Narcissus stayed on to admire it until, in the end, the gods changed him into a flower, and there he lingers still – as you yourself might see if you happened one day on that mountain stream – nodding his yellow head over the water.

JOURNEYS &
CONQUESTS

The quest or trial is a key theme in myth. Through a series of almost impossible tasks, often involving journeys into strange, otherworldly realms, the quest offers the hero (and sometimes the heroine) a chance to prove his worth, to fulfill his destiny and restore the world to its right and proper order.

CHAPTER SIX

In this Hindu myth, the gods and the demons are again at war. The goddess Durgâ is one of several manifestations of Pârvati who was the 'shakti', or female persona, of Shiva. In some versions of the story, Durgâ already exists and does not have to be created out of the combined consciousness of the gods.

DURGA AND THE DEMON

The goddess Pârvati had a skill that many a mortal woman would envy: she could change her identity to suit her mood or circumstance. Sometimes she was just herself, beautiful Pârvati, relaxing on a mountaintop with her husband Shiva, discussing metaphysics and matters of love. Sometimes, when provoked to breaking point by her husband's endless meditating, she would do the same herself in a vain attempt to attract his attention, assuming the identity of the gracious Uma. And sometimes, when her anger was really roused, she would become bloodthirsty Kâli, and then gods and men were wise to stay away.

But there was a time when the gods needed Pârvati's help to defeat a powerful enemy, and to do this she assumed yet another manifestation. This is how it happened …

For many a long year, the gods and the demons had been bitter enemies. Now it so happened, one day, that great celebrating was heard in the demons' camp: a monster had been born to the daughter of the mother of all the demons, and he was destined to lead them to victory! The creature was half-buffalo and half-man, and his name was Mahisa.

Mahisa grew in strength and size and skill,

and became a great champion among his race, and it wasn't long before he led the demons in yet another war against the gods. The fighting was so ferocious that the whole earth shook. The gods could see that they were getting the worst of it.

Brahma, Shiva and Krishna conferred as to what they should do, and then all the gods came together and focused their minds and concentrated their energies and raised an invisible force – a huge and awesome anger. And as the anger came into being, Pârvati felt a new mood sweep over her. Her body tingled, the hairs on her skin prickled, she felt a rush of power through her veins, and four new pairs of arms sprang from her sides – ten arms she now had, each ready to hold a weapon. She had become the goddess Durgâ, who was more dangerous than all the gods and the demons put together – and Durgâ knew exactly how to deal with Mahisa.

Settling herself down in her mountain retreat, she pretended to be a lonely wife, practising self-denial to win the attentions of her husband. And then she waited to see if the fish would take the bait, and sure enough, it did.

Hearing of the beautiful ascetic ignored by her husband, Mahisa came to take a look for himself, having first taken the precaution of disguising himself as an old man. He gazed lasciviously on the beautiful woman he saw pining before him.

'A woman like you, wasting yourself on a man like that! Forget him, come to me, I know how to appreciate a woman … the jar may be old and cracked, but the wine inside is full of vigour …' and he made a move towards her.

'It would take a mightier man than you to win my heart!' replied the goddess scornfully, at which Mahisa threw off his disguise and flew into a furious temper, and began hurling mountaintops about, in his rage.

Now the real battle could begin. Armed and mounted on her lion and with the gods ranged about her, Durgâ faced Mahisa and his army of demons. And the fighting was so ferocious that it made the whole world shake, but in the end, Mahisa found himself standing alone, for all his comrades had been destroyed.

Durgâ threw her noose over him, but Mahisa became a lion.

Durgâ cut off his head, but Mahisa became a man.

Durgâ shot him with her arrows, but Mahisa became an elephant.

Durgâ cut off his trunk, but Mahisa became a buffalo man again.

Durgâ mounted him like a horse, and plunged her lance into his heart, and killed him stone-dead.

And so peace was restored to the world, and Durgâ-Pârvati was able to return to quieter pastimes such as sitting on mountain-tops, meditating, philosophising, and talking of matters of love.

BELOW: DURGÂ DESPATCHES THE DEMON MAHISA BY PIERCING HIS HEART WITH HER LANCE.

The Lugh of this story was one of the Irish gods, the Tuatha Dé Danann, and his name is remembered in the corn harvest festival celebrated on 1 August known generally as Lammas, but in Irish as Lughnasadh.

MASTER OF MANY ARTS

Long ago, when one-eyed giants walked the earth and spirits lived in the hills and something might be had for the wishing of it, Cian son of Dian Cécht married Ethniu daughter of Balor, King of the Isles. And this was a great alliance for Cian was of the Tuatha Dé Danann, the people of the goddess Danann, and Ethniu was of the ancient Fomoire, and since the former had first set foot in Ireland the two races had been enemies.

A son was soon born to Ethniu and Cian, and they called the boy Lugh. Through the blood line of his mother, Lugh was the grandson of Balor, and a dark prophesy surrounded the latter. It was said that one day he would die at the hand of his child's child.

But let us leave Balor and Lugh awhile, and turn to the palace at Tara where the Tuatha Dé

RIGHT: THE HILL OF TARA, IN COUNTY MEATH, IRELAND. TARA WAS THE SEAT OF KINGSHIP AND THE RELIGIOUS AND CULTURAL CENTRE OF ANCIENT IRELAND.

Danann are feasting and where, seated at the head of their table, is Nuadu Airgetlám, Nuadu of the Silver Arm, newly reinstated as their king.

Now it so happened, during the course of this feast, that a young and handsome stranger arrived at the gates of Tara and demanded to be allowed in. 'Who goes there?' the gatekeeper asked, and questioned the stranger as to his craft, for none without a craft could enter Tara's royal walls.

'I am a carpenter,' said the stranger.

'We have a carpenter, we need thee not,' replied the gatekeeper.

'I am a smith,' said the stranger.

'We have a smith, we need thee not,' replied the gatekeeper.

'I am a warrior,' said the stranger.

'We have a warrior, we need thee not,' replied the gatekeeper.

'I am a harper,' said the stranger.

'We have a harper, we need thee not,' replied the gatekeeper.

And so it continued, through smith and poet and historian and sorcerer and leech-doctor and cup-bearer, until at last the stranger demanded:

'Is there any in Tara who is master of all these arts together?' to which the gatekeeper replied that there was none such, and the stranger had then to be given admittance to the royal hall.

And who was this master of so many skills? None other, of course, than Lugh himself, grown to manhood. From that time on, Lugh was known as Samildánach, the 'master of each and every art'. And when Nuadu saw in their midst a hero who might help to release the Tuatha from the bondage of the Fomoire, under whose yoke they had fallen once more, he was glad and he invited Lugh to take his place, and sit in the king's seat for the length of thirteen days.

The battle that was to come, the battle of Mag Tuireadh between the Tuatha and the Fomoire, was seven years in the making, and over the field of war hovered those three spectres of death, the sisters Badb, Macha and the Morrígan, thirsting for blood.

In the forefront of battle was Balor, leader of the Fomoire. Now Balor possessed an awesome weapon – a single, enormous eye that was never opened except on the field of war, with a lid so heavy that it needed the strength of four men to lift it. And the terror of this evil eye was that it rendered powerless any army that looked at it.

On the battlefield too was Lugh, in his battle trance, chanting his war chant and moving across the ground on one foot with only one eye open, carrying his sling. And that is how, in the midst of battle, the grandson came upon his grandfather – the two one-eyed adversaries meeting face to face.

Hearing Lugh's voice, Balor was scornful.

'Who is this puny babbler that dares to confront me?' he roared, and demanded that his eye be opened so that he might gaze upon his foe. The lid was raised and – like David facing Goliath – Lugh deftly raised his sling and shot a stone into his grandfather's giant eye with such force that the eye was pushed right through Balor's head, so that now its destructive gaze was redirected at the Fomoire themselves.

In this way the Fomoire were defeated, and in this way the prophesy that Balor would be killed by his grandson was fulfilled.

SUN GODS

The single eye of both Balor and of Lugh on the field of war suggest that they may have been solar deities, the sun being the Eye of Heaven, and the defeat of one by the other hints at the replacement of one kind of solar worship by another.

LIKE FATHER, LIKE SON

The killing of a father or grandfather by his son or grandson is not uncommon in Indo-European mythology, to which the Celtic tradition belongs – think, for example, of Perseus and his grandfather Acrisius, or Oedipus and his father Laius. Behind the surface of this image lies an ancient archetype reflected in the rights of succession of kings – the 'son' (not necessarily a blood descendant) despatches the 'father' in order to marry the queen-goddess, source of sovereignty. He is therefore the son-lover who in his turn will have to make way for the next 'son', and so on.

PERSEUS AND THE GORGON

Full of fantastical images, this Greek myth is stamped with the storyteller's art – the daughter imprisoned by her father, the rejected baby fished up from the water, the three sisters, the journey to the world's end, and the inevitability of fate are all classic story motifs.

The path of destiny winds a crooked way and desire's path leads straight … but which one of us, travelling through the jumbled maze of life, can truly say, 'I know the path I follow?'

So it was with Acrisius, who sought to walk another path than the one mapped out for him by Fate. Acrisius was king of Argos, and he had learned from the oracle at Delphi that the son to be born to his only daughter Danaë would grow one day to kill him – and what man, knowing the death to come, would not seek to escape it? So the king ordered a subterranean chamber to be built – or, some say, a bronze tower – in which he incarcerated his daughter so that no man might come near her.

But Fate will find a way, and when the god

ABOVE: MEDUSA'S SEVERED HEAD PAINTED ON A LEATHER JOUSTING SHIELD BY MICHELANGELO CARAVAGGIO (1573–1610). IN GREEK TRADITION, MEDUSA'S HEAD WAS PLACED ON THE SHIELD OF ATHENE.

Zeus, looking down from his pinnacle in heaven, saw Danaë weeping all alone, he decided to pay her a visit. Neither stone nor bronze could bar his way, for he became a shower of gold and poured himself through the solid walls of her prison, and into her chamber. And by the time Zeus had left her, Danaë had conceived a child, a boy dusted with the gold of the sun, who would be called Perseus.

When the king discovered that, despite all his efforts, his daughter had given birth to a bastard child, he wished to banish her and her infant and send them as far away as possible, to a place from which the boy might never return to do him harm. So he placed them both in a chest, with a few meagre provisions, and cast them adrift on the sea, leaving them to the mercy of the elements and whatever devouring monsters lurked beneath the waters.

But Fate will find a way, and so it was that the chest with its precious cargo did not sink to the bottom of the sea, as the king had thought, but bobbed along on the waves at the whim of the current, until it washed up on the shores of the island of Seriphos, where it was caught up in the nets of Dictys, brother to Polydectes who was king of the island. Polydectes welcomed the sea-borne strangers, and they went to live in the house of his brother.

Time passed, and in the passing of time,

Perseus grew into a proud young warrior, and in Polydectes desire grew to possess Danaë. Now the king was secretly jealous of Perseus, and wanted to be rid of him so that he might freely press his attentions on his mother. He therefore conceived a cruel plan that would send the young man on a long and perilous journey. He announced to the world that he wished to marry a princess by the name of Hippodameia, and demanded that everyone bring gifts for the wedding – fine horses, furs, silver and gold and jewels by the bucketful would all be gratefully received, he declared.

'But you, Perseus …' said the king, purring like a cat that anticipates the cream, '… you must bring me the most special gift of all. You must bring me the head of Medusa.'

These terrible words stifled all laughter and chatter and a silence fell over all those present, so deep that you could have heard a flea jump in the stillness of it. Not the head of Medusa! Everyone had heard tell of the abhorrent Gorgons, the three winged sisters whose names were Stheno, Euryale, and Medusa. Instead of flesh their hands were of bronze, instead of teeth they had boar tusks, instead of hair a tangle of writhing serpents, and their gaze … well, their gaze was so cold that it turned people to stone. No one had ever faced the Gorgons and lived … and this, of course, was exactly why Polydectes chose Perseus to bring him this particular gift.

But what young man, eager to prove his bravery, can resist a challenge? And so, despite the entreaties of his mother, Perseus grabbed the gauntlet thrown down by Polydectes, and began his quest the very next day.

A journey of a thousand miles, says the sage, begins with the first step, and so it was that Perseus stepped out into the wide, wide world without the faintest idea of where he was headed. All he knew was that the Gorgons were rumoured to live on a barren island at the very ends of the earth. But help often comes in unbidden ways, and as Perseus was standing on the shore wondering which way to go, help came in the form of the goddess Athene and the winged god Hermes, who suddenly appeared before him.

'I have heard of your quest,' said Athene, 'If

BELOW: VISIONS FROM HELL – ETRUSCAN SCULPTURES OF TWO OF THE GORGONS. ALL THREE GORGONS WERE THE DAUGHTERS OF CETO AND PHORCYS, AND SISTERS OF THE GRAEAE.

you want to know where the Gorgons live, ask their sisters the Graeae.' Then she gave him her bronze shield and Hermes gave him his sickle, the only blade that would cut through the Gorgon's scales, and offered to accompany Perseus part of the way.

Perseus and Hermes travelled northward, to the land of dusk that lay in the mists of the sea, where lived the three Grey Sisters – Enyo the Warlike, Pemphredo the Wasp, and Deino the Terror. And when they reached it, they heard, drifting out of the curtain of fog, three querulous voices.

'Give it to me, sister! It's my turn to use it.'

'No, sister, I beg to differ! I think you will recall it is mine.'

'Sister, you are quite mistaken. It is mine!'

The voices belonged to the Graeae and they were quarrelling over the single eye and the single tooth which were all that remained to them on account of their great age, and which they would pass from one to the other as need demanded. Perseus saw his opportunity.

'Good day to you, grandmother,' said he, snatching the eye as it passed from one hand to the next, 'and good day to you,' as he snatched the tooth. 'Excuse my impertinence, dear ladies, but if you wish to see and to eat again, you must tell me where the Gorgons live.'

There was much grumbling and fumbling and groping and grinding of toothless gums, but at last the Graeae replied.

'If you want to know where the Gorgons live,' they croaked in unison, 'you must ask the Hesperides.'

The Hesperides were the Daughters of Night who guarded the Golden Apples of Immortality, in a place beyond the setting sun. Perseus and Hermes made their way there.

'We have heard of your quest,' said the Hesperides, 'and we can tell you where the Gorgons live. Look …' And they pointed to an island, far away on the horizon. 'That is where you will find them.'

The Hesperides also gave Perseus gifts to help him in his quest: winged sandals so that he might fly as fast as Hermes; a helmet belonging to Hades, God of the Underworld, that rendered the wearer invisible; and a magic pouch in which to place the Gorgon's head. With these, and with the shield of Athene and the sickle of Hermes also, Perseus set off alone to complete the task for which he had come.

Hovering over the island of the Gorgons

BELOW: WATCHED BY ATHENE, PERSEUS BRANDISHES THE HEAD OF MEDUSA TO TURN POLYDECTES TO STONE, IN A PAINTING BY JEAN-MARC NATTIER (1685–1766).

LEFT: AN ATHENIAN COIN, DATING FROM ABOUT 550 BC, SHOWING THE LEERING HEAD OF A GORGON.

like a great bird, Perseus looked down and saw that this desolate spot was littered with rocks of all shapes and sizes, some tall, some short, some wide, some thin … rocks that had once been people metamorphosed by the stony stare of the Gorgons – and there, in their midst, were the three sisters themselves, asleep, with their serpent locks wriggling over their faces.

Now of the three Gorgons, the only one who was mortal, the only one who could be killed, was Medusa, and that is why she was the one whom Perseus attacked. Taking care not to look in her face lest she wake and catch his eye, he held up Athene's shield so that he could see Medusa's reflection in it, and then, guided by this mirror image, raised the sickle of Hermes and sliced through the Gorgon's neck like a butcher cleaving a carcass.

The instant the head was severed, chaos broke out. A fountain of blood gushed from the neck and out of this bloody tide rode a flying horse, Pegasus by name; Stheno and Euryale woke up and looked about to see what had disturbed their sleep; and as for Perseus, he grabbed Medusa's head, stuffed it in the magic pouch, and made off, flying faster than a look goes between a man and a maid, with the Gorgons in vain pursuit, for how could they catch someone they could not see?

Stopping off in Ethiopia on his way back to Seriphos, Perseus had a fateful encounter, for it was here that he came upon Andromeda, who had been chained to a rock as a sacrifice to a sea monster and was waiting to be devoured. He fell in love with her at first sight, cut through her bonds, and took her home with him to be his wife.

When he arrived back at the palace of Polydectes, Perseus discovered that, during his absence, his mother Danaë had been cruelly treated by the king. He approached the throne.

'Sire,' he said, 'here is your wedding gift,' and he pulled the head of Medusa out of the magic pouch and held it up before the king, whereupon Polydectes was instantly turned to stone … and if that stone has not crumbled, it stands there still.

Perseus then gave the head to Athene, who placed it on her shield, and he, Danaë and Andromeda left Seriphos and sailed for Argos, where Acrisius his grandfather still lived. Now Acrisius had never forgotten the oracle's prophesy and, hearing that Perseus was still alive and, worse still, heading his way, he fled in terror to the city of Larissa in Thessaly, in an attempt to escape his prophesied death.

But Fate will find a way, and it so happened that the ship bearing Perseus was blown off course to this same Larissa, where the people were holding their annual games, watched by King Acrisius. A skilled athlete, Perseus was invited to join in the sport. Holding a discus in his hand, he began the wide curve of the throw. The discus left his hand and soared through the air in a mighty arc but, just as it was winging its way downward, a freak gust blew it toward the crowd of spectators, and there it met its mark: it struck Acrisius full on the forehead and killed him, stock stone dead.

And so, in the end, all the efforts of Acrisius did not save him from the death that awaited him, and the winding path of destiny that began in Argos ended in Larissa, just as Fate had planned all along.

Hercules, also known as Herakles, the hero of this classical Greek myth, was a forerunner of all the muscled macho men of contemporary cinema. Son of Zeus – inevitably – he becomes increasingly invincible with age.

THE COMING OF HERCULES

Throughout all of Greece it was well known that Hercules was the strongest and bravest man in the land – and how could it be otherwise, with Perseus, slayer of the dreaded snake-haired Medusa, for his grandfather, and his father rumoured to be none other than Zeus himself?

It all began simply enough, one warm night in Thebes, Amphitryon, King of Thebes and son of Perseus, was away at the wars, and had left his wife Alcmene, also a child of Perseus, alone in the palace. Looking down from his pinnacle on Mount Olympus, Zeus found the scene irresistible – a beautiful young queen all on her own with no one to share her bed … The poor girl could do with a little comfort, he was sure. So he stole down to earth and, assuming the appearance of the absent king – down to the very last hair on his chin – persuaded her to lie with him. When the real king, returned from battle, arrived in her bedroom a day or two later, the queen was pleasantly surprised to find his ardour undimmed, and from this double union came a double birth – twin boys, one of whom was Iphicles and the other Hercules.

On the day that Alcmene was due to deliver Hercules, Zeus – proud prospective father that he was – made a pronouncement from heaven: the descendant of Perseus that was about to be born would one day be king of all Greece! When Hera, Zeus' long-suffering wife, heard her husband's latest nonsense, she decided she would have none of it. Why should

ABOVE: THE PRECOCIOUS INFANT HERCULES STRANGLES THE TWO SNAKES SENT TO KILL HIM, ON THIS COIN MADE IN ABOUT 350 BC.

some brat born to yet another of her wayward spouse's mortal bedfellows be allowed such an honour as this? No, she would put a stop to it. So she went at once to Thebes and by means of her divine power prolonged the labour of Alcmene so that another boy child was delivered ahead of him. This was Eurystheus son of Sthenelus – and because this child, too, was a descendant of Perseus, Zeus was forced to recognize him as the future king.

This would not be the last time that Eurystheus, guided by the hand of Hera, would muddy the pool of Hercules' fortunes.

But to return awhile to the childhood of Hercules. Part-hero, part-god, it was only natural that the boy should show signs of precociousness early on. One night, when all the palace was fast asleep and Hercules was still a baby, two snakes – undoubtedly sent by Hera – came slithering across the nursery floor, intent on killing the boy. But while Ipiphicles, who was alongside his brother, screamed in terror, Hercules showed no fear but simply picked the serpents up – one in each pink, plump, dimpled hand – and squeezed their necks until they were dead.

As Hercules grew up, he was taught all the things that noble Greek youths should know – how to play the lyre, how to reason and argue, how to drive a chariot, how to shoot arrows from a bow. He also spent some time living among herdsmen in the mountains, and it was here that he developed his extraordinary physical strength and heavily muscled body.

At the age of eighteen, while lying in wait for a ferocious lion that had been attacking Amphitryon's herds, Hercules took up brief residence in the house of King Thespius. Now this king had fifty beautiful young daughters and Hercules, who was temporarily unoccupied, whiled away the empty hours by lying with all fifty maidens in a single night … like father, like son, some might say.

But life is not always an upward path, even for divine heroes, and Hercules was about to feel the hand of Hera again. Throughout his growing years she had been keeping an eye on him, and decided it was now time to interfere in his life again.

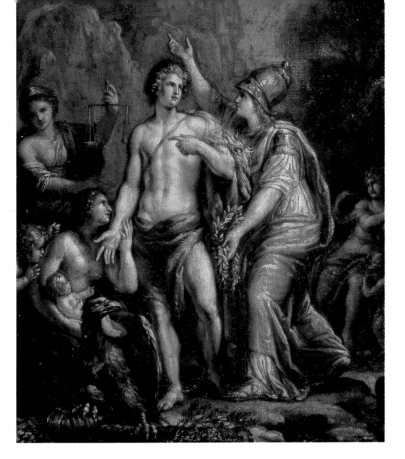

By this time, Hercules had married. His wife was Megara, daughter of King Creon of Orchomenus, but their marriage, sadly, was not a happy one, and Hera was quick to seize her opportunity. She sent one of the vengeful Furies – spirit sisters born of the blood of murdered Uranus – to torment him and drive him mad. Day after day, the Fury was with him, never leaving his side, whispering dark thoughts in his ear, until in the end he lost all reason and fell on his own wife and children and murdered them.

When he came to his senses and saw what he had done, Hercules was horrified, and went to Delphi to consult the oracle there, as to what he should do to expiate the hideous crime he had committed. And the oracle told him that he must place himself in the service of Eurystheus, his cousin and old rival, and do whatsoever the king commanded him to do.

And that is when Hercules' real trials began, for it would be twelve full years before the stain of his sin was removed.

This epic saga of atonement is the most famous part of the life story of the Greek hero Hercules. The Pillars of Hercules, beyond which lay the Garden of the Hesperides which Hercules visits, would, on a modern map, be the Straits of Gibraltar.

THE LABOURS OF HERCULES

In the palace at Mycenæ, Hercules stood before the throne of King Eurytheus, his cousin and the man who had, by virtue of his birth, robbed Hercules of the crown. He was there, under the orders of the oracle at Delphi, to offer himself in service to the king, so that he might atone for the crazed murder of his own wife and children. An act of humility such as this was not easy, for a man as brave and strong as he.

The king looked Hercules over. He saw the

Above: As his first Labour, Hercules was enjoined to kill the Nemean lion. He can be seen doing so here, in a detail from a Greek vase painting from the first half of the 5th century BC.

rippling muscles of his body under the golden sheen of his skin. He noticed, too, the flutter that Hercules' arrival was causing among the ladies of the court, and he was, well … jealous.

'Just look at him …' the king brooded to himself, 'so swaggering and brave and bold. Well, he'll not be so proud when I've finished with him.' With Hercules in servitude to him, he could command him to do anything he liked! And he began to think of all the impossible tasks he could set the hero that would teach him a little humility – if they didn't kill him first, that is.

THE LION OF NEMEA

'There is a lion …' Eurystheus began, '… in Nemea. You know the one – I'm sure you have heard of it. Well, it's causing a little spot of bother over there. Go and kill it for me, there's a good fellow – oh, and bring me back the skin when you've finished.'

Hercules had no choice but to obey. Now this lion was a terrifying beast that had been killing sheep and cattle all around, even taking a child or two, and none in its vicinity felt safe.

When Hercules first came upon his adversary, he tried to kill it with his arrows, but they just seemed to glance off the animal's pelt. There was nothing else for it – he would have to use his bare hands. With a great shout, Hercules fell on the lion. Hair flew and fur flew and blood flew, but in the end the monster lay dead at Hercules' feet. He had strangled it, just as he had strangled the two snakes when he was a baby.

When Hercules appeared at the palace again, not only alive and well but also triumphantly wearing the lion's skin over his shoulder in the most nonchalant manner, Eurystheus was not well pleased.

What labour could he set him next?

THE HYDRA OF LERNA

'I hear you're a bit of a snake killer,' said the king. 'Well, over in Lerna there's a serpent I'd like you to deal with … has nine heads, so I'm told, but that shouldn't be too much of a problem for you. See to it for me, will you?'

Hercules had no choice but to obey. The Hydra – for that was the serpent's name – did indeed have nine heads and poisonous breath as well. It lived in the marshes, where it ravaged both crops and herds and, with the poison it breathed out, killed anyone who came near it.

Accompanied by his nephew Iolaus, Hercules set off for Lerna. Once arrived there, he enticed the monster out into the open by means of flaming arrows, and attempted to strike off its heads with his powerful club. But for every head that rolled, two new ones grew. The task seemed impossible, until Iolaus had the bright idea of setting a neighbouring forest alight and, with blazing brands taken from the fire, burning the heads instead. When all but

LEFT: IN A PAINTING BY ANTONIO POLLAIOLO (1432/3–98), HERCULES CLUBS EACH OF THE NINE HEADS OF THE HYDRA. HOWEVER, IT WAS ONLY WITH THE HELP OF IOLAUS THAT THE HERO WOULD SUCCEED IN THIS LABOUR.

the last head was gone, Hercules cut off that one, too, and buried it. Then he dipped his arrows in the Hydra's poisonous blood to make them even more deadly.

When Hercules appeared at the palace again, not only alive and well but also carrying a quiver of fatal arrows that meant certain death to any of their victims, Eurystheus was not well pleased.

What labour could he set him next?

THE BOAR OF ERYMANTHUS

'They tell me that over on Mount Erymanthus they're being bothered by a wild boar,' began the king, 'Well, when I heard that I naturally thought of you, so big, so strong, so brave ... Go over there and deal with it for me – oh, and this time, bring the animal back alive.'

Hercules had no choice but to obey. It was Eurystheus' hope that, on the long return journey the boar, enraged at being captured, would take the opportunity to gore the hero to death.

Hercules duly set off for the mountain, but was slightly interrupted in his errand by some rowdy centaurs, creatures who were half-man, half-horse, on whom he was forced to use his poisoned arrows. At last, though, he arrived at his destination and spotted his quarry. The boar had huge tusks whose tips were as sharp as razors. It was about to charge Hercules, when the hero deftly stooped down, lifted the animal up, and slung it over his shoulders.

When Hercules appeared at the palace again, with a snuffling, snorting wild boar draped around his shoulders as if it were no more than an ermine collar, Eurystheus was terrified and hid in a bronze jar. But inside the jar, he was seething with rage: this fellow Hercules was far too cocky for his own good.

What labour could he set him next?

THE BIRDS OF STYMPHALUS

'You have heard of the marshes of Stymphalus?' said the king. 'Well, the people thereabouts are complaining that they cannot graze their beasts or go about their business for fear of attack by birds – never heard such nonsense myself, but if I'm to get any peace go and do what you must to calm them down.'

Hercules had no choice but to obey. Now the devious king knew all too well why the people of the region were afraid, for these were no ordinary birds but winged creatures with beaks and claws of iron, and feathers so sharp that their tips were like nails, and in their flight the birds would loose these feathers like a shower of knives onto any living thing below. When they rose from the marshes, they were so numerous that they blotted out the sun.

For these adversaries, Hercules decided on a slightly different course of action from usual. Instead of trying to kill them, which would have been near impossible because of their numbers, he called them out by banging with his lance on his shield – held over his head for protection – and at the same time ringing a large bell.

Now as any farmer will tell you, birds are afraid of loud noises, and in that respect these birds were no different from any others. Startled by the shattering din that Hercules was making, they rose in vast clouds from the marshes, scattering their feathers as they went, and flew away. Those few that remained Hercules was easily able to despatch with his poisoned arrows.

When Hercules appeared at the palace again, alive and well and with not one scratch on him, Eurystheus was not well pleased.

What labour could he set him next?

THE HIND OF CERYNEIA

'I have a fancy,' the king mused, 'to see the stag that roams the forests on Mount Cernyneia. Her horns are made of gold and her hooves of bronze, but she is so fleet of foot that no hunter has yet been able to catch her – but for someone as brave and clever as you, I'm sure it will be an easy task ...'

Hercules had no choice but to obey. As he set off on his quest, Eurystheus pictured what would happen – the strong man running and running, the sweat pouring from his body, yet unable to catch the hind who remained tantalizingly always just out of reach, and at last collapsing and dying from exhaustion. The king felt a warm glow of pleasure as he gazed on the imaginary scene. There was added danger, too, in that the hind was rumoured to be under the protection of Artemis, Goddess of Hunting. Oh yes, this would surely be the end of this so-called son of Zeus!

Well, the picture in the king's mind was not dissimilar from what really happened. Hercules came upon the beautiful hind in the forest, and the chase began. The hero was fast on his feet, but the hind was faster, and she led him over hill and down dale, up mountains and through rivers, out into lands he had never known. But instead of collapsing from exhaustion, Hercules just kept on running and running until a whole year had gone by and the chase had come full circle back to where it began. There stood the panting hind, unable to run any longer, and Hercules would have laid his hands on her then and there had he not looked up and seen, in the light of the full moon, the goddess Artemis standing before him. She forbade him to touch the hind, for the animal belonged to her, but told him to return to Eurystheus with news of all that had passed, and to consider his fifth labour done.

When Hercules appeared at the palace again, alive and well after a whole year away, and told how he had caught the hind but set it free, and spoke of his meeting with the goddess, Eurystheus was not well pleased – in fact, he was not a little irritated.

What labour could he set him next?

THE STABLES OF AUGEIAS

'My friend King Augeias,' began Eurystheus, 'is having a lot of trouble with his stablehands. He can't get them to stay, you see, because of the state of the stables. They are filthy! The dung has been piling up for years now, and as for the stench … I told him I knew just the man for the job – you!'

Hercules had no choice but to obey. Eurystheus chuckled to himself as he thought of his brave and proud cousin knee-deep in cattle dung, getting it under his nails and in his skin and, with any luck, in his hair, too. This was the best labour yet!

Faced with such an onerous task, you or I would heave a deep sigh and pick up a shovel – but that was not Hercules' way. No, what he

chose to do was to make a breach in the stable wall and divert the course of two rivers, the Alpheus and Peneius, so that they ran through the stables like a great jet of water and sluiced out the accumulated ordure of decades.

When Hercules appeared at the palace again, alive and well and looking as fresh and clean as a new morning, Eurystheus was not well pleased. Getting rid of Hercules was proving more of a problem than he thought.

What labour could he set him next?

THE BULL OF CRETE

'I am sending you over to Crete,' said the king. 'I hear the country is being terrorized by a mad bull. I'm sure the Cretans would appreciate a little help from you.'

Hercules had no choice but to obey. Now this animal was, of course, none other than the white bull sent from the sea by the god Poseidon, in proof of the right of Minos to the throne of Crete. In return, Minos should have sacrificed the animal, but he substituted another in its place. Even a king, however, cannot deceive a god, and the punishment for his disobedience was terrible: first Poseidon made the king's wife fall in love with the bull, and then he drove the bull mad. Having coupled with the queen, the crazed animal then roamed the island so that it was hardly safe to venture out.

But such trifles were all in a day's work for our hero. He captured the bull and, hoisting the animal onto his back, returned with his latest gift to Eurystheus.

When Hercules appeared at the palace again, alive and well and with a white bull draped across his back, Eurystheus was not well pleased. He ground his teeth in anger.

What labour could he set him next?

THE MARES OF DIOMEDES

'I want some new breeding stock for my stable of horses,' began the king, 'and I believe that the mares of King Diomedes are just the fresh blood I need. Ask him if he will agree.'

Hercules had no choice but to obey. Now these were no ordinary mares, but terrifying creatures fed on human flesh – and it was Eurystheus' hope that Hercules would provide their next meal.

Hercules set off and, with the help of a few others, captured the mares, whereupon the men of Diomedes descended on them and a ferocious battle ensued. Inevitably, Hercules was victorious, and fed the wicked Diomedes to his own mares.

BELOW: A GRAND FINALE. IN THIS DRAWING BY PIETRO DA CORTONA (1596–1669) HERCULES CONTEMPLATES SOME OF HIS TROPHIES – THE LION, THE HYDRA, THE BOAR, THE HIND, THE BULL, THE MARES AND THE HOUND.

While on this little excursion, he also found the time to fight Thanatos – Death – himself, for the life of Queen Alcestis of Pherae.

When Hercules appeared at the palace again, alive and well and with not a lump of flesh missing, Eurystheus was not well pleased. Could nothing get the better of his cousin?

What labour could he set him next?

THE GIRDLE OF HIPPOLYTE

'My daughter Admete is bored with her jewels,' said Eurystheus. 'She has a yearning for the Girdle of Hippolyte, and says she will die if she does not have it. Bring it to me!'

Hercules had no choice but to obey. Eurystheus, of course, was fully aware of where he was sending his cousin, for Hippolyte was queen of the Amazons, fierce warrior women, and her girdle – a gorgeous, richly decorated adornment – had been given her by Ares, the God of War, as a mark of her sovereignty. Eurystheus could not see a woman like that parting readily with a gift from a god.

After several adventures, Hercules at last reached the country where Hippolyte and her Amazons lived. At first, surprisingly, the queen seemed willing to hand over her girdle but Hera, who always kept a close eye on the affairs of Hercules, thought that things were going too smoothly and decided that it was time to sow a little discord. So she spread a rumour that Hercules had secretly come to abduct Hippolyte, whereupon the Amazons – like soldier ants defending their queen – seized their weapons and made ready to attack. Hercules, in turn, believing that they had intended to capture him all along, retaliated and slaughtered them all, including the queen.

When Hercules appeared at the palace again, alive and well and with barely a scratch and not a hair out of place, Eurystheus was not well pleased. His cousin was beginning to look horribly invincible.

What labour could he give him next?

THE CATTLE OF GERYON

Eurystheus had a problem. Since Hercules had been in action, there were hardly any monsters or nameless terrors left for any self-respecting hero to confront ... but Eurystheus would come up with one, even if it meant sending Hercules to the ends of the earth. And that is exactly what he did.

'I hear you once lived amongst herdsmen,' he said. 'Well, I have just the job for a man who has a way with cattle. I want you to bring me the red cattle of Geryon.'

Hercules had no choice but to obey. What Eurystheus hadn't mentioned was that this Geryon was in fact a fearsome giant, with three bodies and three heads, six legs and six arms, and a pair of wings for good measure. He had an enormous herd of red cattle which, at night, he drove into a dark cave. What was more, he lived as far as it is possible to go, on an island that lay beyond the setting sun.

In order to reach this alien place, Hercules borrowed the golden cup belonging to the Sun God Helios, in which the god would sail every night, from west to east, after he had slipped behind the horizon. The cup also had the additional advantage of being able to enlarge or decrease in size, depending on the needs of the person using it.

Arrived on the island, Hercules set to work. First he had to kill Geryon's watchdog, then his herdsman, and then he saw Geryon himself – all flailing arms and swinging clubs, and roaring from all his three throats at once – coming towards him. The hero lifted his bow, let fly his poisoned arrows, and the giant fell dead on the spot before he had the chance to advance any closer.

Hercules herded all the cattle into the cup of Helios, which obligingly swelled to accommodate them. The return journey involved a few dramas – the sons of Poseidon the sea god tried to steal the cattle, and at one stopping place Hera stampeded the animals by tormenting them with a gadfly. Hercules also managed to find the time, along the way, to put an end to human sacrifice in Gaul.

It was a busy time for our hero.

When, at last, he appeared at the palace again, alive and well and with a huge herd of cattle trotting along meekly behind him, Eurystheus was not well pleased. Ten labours accomplished, ten victories to boast about,

Hercules had no choice but to obey. The fruits of which the king spoke were the golden apples of eternal life that grew in a paradise garden to the far west, beyond the sunset. They were tended by three sisters called the Hesperides, and around the tree on which they grew wound a dragon whose name was Ladon.

Although everyone had heard of this wonderful garden, no one knew exactly how to get there. Hercules set off to find it, going in a north-westerly direction – but trouble lay waiting at every turn for, like a gunfighter whose reputation precedes him, he was a magnet to every monster, every giant, every villain, every have-a-go hero.

By the River Rhone, nymphs told him to ask the way of Nereus, the Sea God. Hercules captured Nereus and waited patiently while the god went through the whole tiresome business of shape-shifting, until at last, seeing that Hercules was unimpressed, he told him he must go southward.

In the Caucasus Hercules freed Prometheus whose liver was being eaten by an eagle. In Egypt, he escaped being offered as a human sacrifice. In Libya, he fought a terrible giant, son of Gaea the Earth Mother, who drew new strength every time his foot touched the ground, vanquishing him by holding him up in the air. Sleeping after his struggle with the giant, he was attacked by Pygmies in his sleep, but he sewed them up into his lion skin. At last, as he neared his destination, he saw the man he had been looking for – Atlas, the giant whose job it was to carry the whole world on his shoulders.

Seeing how weary he looked, Hercules offered to take the weight off his shoulders for a while if he, in return, would bring him three of the golden apples. No sooner said than done, for the Hesperides were the daughters of

and Hercules was still standing. The man was totally impossible!

What labour could he set him next?

THE APPLES OF PARADISE

Eurystheus was beginning to lose patience. If he had sent him to the ends of the earth once, he would send him there again, and perhaps this time it would work.

'In a garden far away grows a tree that bears magical apples,' said the king, 'and I have a desire to taste them. Fetch me some.'

ABOVE LEFT: IN A PAINTING BY BARTHOLOMUS SPRANGER (1546–1611) HERCULES RESCUES DEIANIRA FROM THE CENTAUR NESSUS. IT WAS NESSUS' POISONOUS BLOOD THAT WOULD BE THE CAUSE OF HERCULES' DEATH.

Atlas and happily gave him some of their fruit.

When Hercules appeared at the palace again, alive and well and bearing three golden fruits in his hand, Eurystheus was not well pleased. Eleven labours completed, two journeys to the ends of the earth! He was running out of ideas.

What labour could he set him next?

THE HOUND OF HELL

Eurystheus thought and thought, and at last came up with a fiendishly cunning plan. If Hercules could go to the ends of the earth and back, how would he feel about going to hell and back?

'There are so many thieves about these days.' the king began, 'What I really need to protect me is a good watchdog – and the best one I know is Cerberus who guards the gates of hell. I want him and no other.'

Hercules had no choice but to obey. Now this Cerberus was a terrifying hound, with three heads and slavering jaws and eyes like saucers, and he was guard dog to Hades, god of the underworld. Guided by Hermes, the messenger of the gods, Hercules made his way into the infernal regions and after various obstacles stood at last before the throne of Hades, who agreed to allow Hercules to take the animal on condition that he conquered him with nothing but his bare hands.

Now this was just the sort of challenge our hero relished, and when he and Cerberus engaged in their struggle, well, you could not tell which was man and which was dog for all the growling and the howling and the grappling and the ripping and the twisting and the tearing. But at last, with Hercules' hands firmly around his throats, Cerberus conceded defeat, and Hercules dragged him by the scruff of one of his necks back to Eurystheus.

When Hercules appeared at the palace again, alive and well and with the hound of hell padding along behind him like some docile puppy, Eurystheus threw up his hands.

'I give up!' he said. 'No one and nothing can beat you.'

Hercules had successfully completed every one of the twelve labours he had been set, and

he had removed the stain of his sin: he was absolved of his crime, and he parted company with Eurystheus.

But a man must do what a man must do and Hercules, never one for the quiet, stay-at-home life, continued to have many more adventures. In the end, he died at the hands of his second wife Deianeira, who innocently smeared his robe with the poisonous blood of a centaur, believing it to be a love potion. The robe stuck to his skin and tore off his flesh. Lying on a funeral pyre of his own making, Hercules ascended to heaven in a burst of thunder and lightning, and was there reconciled with Hera and married to her daughter Hebe and lived with her in the bliss and glory of eternal life.

And what man – or hero – could possibly ask for more?

KEEPERS OF THE GATE

When Hercules makes his journey to and from the afterworld – the greatest initiation rite of all – whom else should he encounter there, standing at the threshold between this world and the next, but a dog? Perhaps because of its flesh-eating habits, the dog has particularly strong associations with death. As a psychopomp, it was the dog that guided souls through the gateway from the land of the living into the realm of the dead.

ANUBIS

The Egyptian 'keeper of the gate' was Anubis, the Jackal God or Great Dog who guarded the Egyptian underworld.

THE MOON

In its imagery of a pair of dogs guarding a pathway leading towards the moon, the moon card of the Tarot pack recalls the ancient Hindu concept of the Moon as the gateway to the afterworld, guarded by the two dogs of the Death Goddess.

THE HOUNDS OF HEL

In Norse myth, the moon-dogs who carried away the dead belonged to the goddess Angurboda, the 'Hag of the Iron Wood', and an older incarnation of the goddess Hel, Queen of the Dead.

THE HOUNDS OF ANNWN

In the mythology of the British Celts, these were the dogs of Arawn, King of Annwn, the dreamy, otherworldly land of death.

Beneath the Hellenic surface of this classical Greek saga, which culminates with the famous episode of Theseus and the Minotaur, the echoes of an older tale may be heard – a tale of ritual sacrifice and sacred marriage to ensure the continuing powers of a king.

THE BULLS FROM THE SEA

In a bull ring at Knossos on the island of Crete youths and maidens vault over the horns of a bull, twirling and turning and tumbling in a joyful dance, as if oblivious of death.

In a ship at the port of Athens seven youths and seven maidens set sail for Knossos, fearful of death on the horns of a monster that is half-bull and half-man.

What story connects these two images? A family saga that spans the generations, a tale whose fabric is woven of the threads of lust and abduction, madness and murder, the pattern of its weaving repeating itself to infinity, like mirror image reflecting mirror image.

And wherever you look into the fragments of this ancient tale, always, always, in the centre of each picture, is the Bull.

And so the story begins.

THE PRIESTESS AND THE BULL

At the shrine of the Heraion, near the town of Argos in southern Greece, a priestess of Hera by the name of Io was performing her sacred duties. Her activities did not go unnoticed. Looking down from his pinnacle in heaven Zeus – brother and husband to Hera, Bull-god and great philanderer – espied the lovely Io, and was overcome by passionate desire. And so, in the guise of a cloud, he descended to earth, and claimed Io as his own.

In order to deceive Hera, Zeus changed his mistress into a white cow. But Hera was not to be fooled that easily. No sooner had the transformation taken place than she asked her husband for the pretty little heifer as a gift. Outmanoevred, what could Zeus do but consent? Hera then placed her new acquisition under the care of Argus Panoptes – 'he who sees all' – a giant with one hundred eyes, only fifty of which were ever closed in sleep while the other fifty remained watchfully open.

And so Hera thought to have won the game, but Zeus had another card to play. He sent Hermes, messenger of the gods, to charm Argus with the music of his flute, and when all one hundred of the giant's eyes had closed in an enchanted sleep, Hermes cut off his head, and Io made good her escape.

When Hera discovered that she had been outwitted, she tore out all of Argus' eyes and tossed them into the tail of her peacock, and there you may see them to this day, winking at you still. As for the unfortunate Io, Hera sent after her a stinging insect – a gadfly – to pursue her wherever she went, to harass her and bite her and suck her blood. And so the tauropárthenos, the virgin dedicated to the bull, was forced to flee.

In wild torment, like a stag before the hounds, the white cow plunged into the sea and, with the buzzing of her torturer for ever spurring her on, she crossed and re-crossed the waters, going now east, now west, in a crazed attempt to escape what she could not, traversing first the Bosphorus, then the sea which now bears her name, the Ionian, until at last, swimming eastward, she came ashore in the land of Egypt. And here Zeus gently skimmed his hand over her like a breeze skimming the tree-tops, and she regained her human form.

LEFT: SURROUNDED BY HER HANDMAIDENS, EUROPA RIDES ON THE BACK OF THE GARLANDED WHITE BULL. THE PAINTING IS BY HENDRICK VAN BALEN (C.1575–1632).

And when a child was born of their union, Io called him Epaphus, which means 'a hand's light touch'. But some say he was also Apis – Apis the Bull God of Egypt....

But that is not the end of the story.

THE PRINCESS AND THE BULL

In Phoenicia in Asia Minor, in a meadow by the sea, a group of girls were gathering flowers. One of them was princess Europa, 'she of the wide eyes' who also, it so happened, was descended from the white cow Io.

In her innocent pastime, Europa did not go unnoticed. Looking down from his pinnacle in heaven, Zeus espied her and was overcome by passionate desire. And so, in the guise of a bull, he descended to earth.

Hearing a soft snort behind her, Europa turned and saw there such a pretty sight – a beautiful bull, with flanks and horns as white as ivory. She approached the animal who seemed tame enough. She laughed with delight as the bull allowed her to stroke his nose and to garland his horns with flowers, and her delight increased even further when her charming pet bowed down and allowed her to climb on his back.

The beast rose and Europa waved to her handmaidens – 'Look at me! I'm riding on the back of a bull!' – and the bull began to trot towards the sea, and the trot became a canter and the canter became a gallop, and before Europa could call 'Stop!', the bull had plunged into the frothing and foaming waves. On and on he surged through the rolling swell, swimming ever westward, with the terrified princess clinging to his horns, until at last they came ashore on the island of Crete.

And there, under a plane tree, the union of Europa and Zeus was consummated, and the child of their union was Minos, who would be King of Crete. And Europa of the wide eyes, the child's Asian mother, gave her name to this alien region to which she had been forcibly carried: it was called Europe.

But that is not the end of the story.

THE KING AND THE BULL

In his palace at Knossos on the island of Crete, King Minos was pacing the floor. A burning dispute had arisen between him and his brothers, Rhadamanthys and Sarpedon, over the possession of the throne. Minos turned to Poseidon, God of the Sea, and prayed to him to send him a bull as a sign that the kingship was rightfully his. In return, he promised the god that he would immediately offer the animal up in sacrifice.

Out of the realm of the Sea King, out of the blue Mediterranean waves, there then arose a magnificent bull, with flanks and horns as white as ivory. What a splendid beast it was, far too splendid, Minos thought, to die on the blade of sacrifice. And so he substituted another in its stead, believing that Poseidon would not know the difference.

But Poseidon did know, and to punish Minos for his crime of disobedience, the god fixed his gaze on Pasiphaë, the wife of Minos, and fuelled in her a passionate desire for the

Left: Theseus prepares to plunge his sword into the body of the Minotaur, the 'monster in the maze', in this detail from a Greek vase.

white bull. Maddened with longing, Pasiphaë went to Daedalos, the cunning craftsman from Athens, and asked him to make for her a model of a cow in which she might hide. And so it was done. In the outward form of a cow, Pasiphaë approached the bull, her beloved, and the bull was deceived and mated with her.

And the fruit of this union was a monster, an aberration, a thing – a deformed creature with the head of a bull and the body of a man. And the creature was called the Minotaur, the 'Minos-bull'.

To hide Pasiphaë's shame, Daedalos was again summoned, this time by the king, and asked to build a covered maze of twisting and tortuous passages in which the monster could be for ever concealed. And so it was done, and the labyrinth constructed by Daedalos hid the dark secret that lay at the heart of the palace at Knossos, the royal city on the island of Crete.

But that is not the end of the story.

THE MONSTER IN THE MAZE

On a quay in the port of Athens, a group of seven youths and seven maidens, shivering with fear and weeping, were boarding a ship with black sails. The vessel was bound for Knossos, and the unfortunates now taking their places on deck were the latest tribute, paid every eight years by the citizens of Athens, to the conqueror Minos of Crete, in recompense for the murder of his son Androgeus. They knew all too well the fate that awaited them. Once arrived at Knossos, they would be taken to a labyrinth tenanted by a hideous monster, half-bull and half-man, that had a taste for human flesh – and this time the flesh on which he gorged would be theirs.

But on this particular voyage, the third of its kind, there was one among their number of the most exalted birth; this was Theseus, son of Poseidon God of the Sea, and adopted son of Aegeus, King of Athens. Now Theseus had a secret mission. Among the company destined to be sacrificed to the Cretan bull, he would enter the labyrinth and there he would slay the monstrous Minotaur, and thus set Athens free. If he met with success, he told Aegeus, he would hoist white sails on the returning ship; if

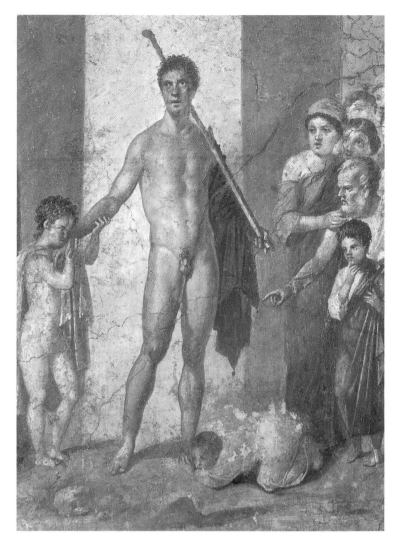

ABOVE: IN THIS POMPEIAN FRESCO DATING FROM AD 59–70, THESEUS, WATCHED BY THE PEOPLE OF KNOSSOS, LEADS THE MINOTAUR'S INTENDED VICTIMS OUT OF THE LABYRINTH, WHILE THE MONSTER HIMSELF LIES DEAD AT HIS FEET.

he failed, the sails on the ship would be black.

When the victims arrived at Knossos, Theseus – insouciant, brave and bold – boasted of his divine parentage, saying that he was the son of the God of the Sea. To test his claim, Minos tossed a ring into the waters and told Theseus to bring it back, whereupon Theseus dived in and retrieved not only the ring but brought up another trophy, too – the crown of Amphitrite, Queen of the Sea.

Watching this show of bravado was the princess Ariadne, daughter of Minos and half-sister to the Minos-bull, and she was greatly taken with this handsome stranger

from Athens. Catching her gaze, Theseus approached her and placed on her head the crown from the sea, and Ariadne's fate was sealed. Her heart filled with such love for Theseus that she was prepared to betray her own father to save him.

Once again, the help of Daedalos was sought. And what did the cunning Daedalos give Ariadne to aid her beloved in his quest? A sword, a dagger, an axe? No, what he gave her was nothing more than a simple ball of twine.

And Theseus took the twine and, unravelling it, made his way to the very heart of the gloomy labyrinth, where he plunged his fatal sword into the raging Minotaur's flank, and then followed the same path back, fingering his way through the darkness along the trail of twine and out into the light.

Now it was not safe for Ariadne to remain in Knossos, so she fled the island with Theseus, and they set sail for his home in Athens.

But that is not the end of the story.

THE PRINCESS AND THE BULL
Gently pitching and rolling on the rise and fall of the waves, the ship with Theseus and Ariadne on board was making its way northward from Crete to Athens. But halfway through the voyage, Theseus decided to drop anchor at the island of Naxos. Exhausted after her hurried escape from Knossos, Ariadne lay down on the sands by the sea and fell asleep. And while she was thus sleeping, Theseus betrayed her. Careless of all she had done for him, he set sail without her, leaving Ariadne desolate and alone, on the island of Naxos.

In Athens, meanwhile, King Aegeus was anxiously waiting for his son's return, looking out from his vantage point on a rocky head-

land for a glimpse of a white sail. But Theseus, in the excitement of victory, had forgotten to change the sails, as he had promised he would. So when Aegeus, screening his old eyes against the sun as he scanned the horizon, saw a ship with black sails, he believed his son to be dead and threw himself from the cliff, and his body, smashed and splintered by the rocks, sank to the bottom of the sea.

And now Fate begins to draw together the threads of this tangled web, to tie them off in a finishing knot, for the weaving of the tale is almost done.

After the death of Aegeus, Theseus becomes King of Athens, and marries Ariadne's sister, Phaedra. Yet still the spectre of the bull will not be laid to rest, for Theseus who has killed a bull will again kill with a bull. On discovering that Phaedra's honour has been sullied by his son Hippolytus – or so the incestuous queen claims – Theseus will call on his father Poseidon to avenge her. And so one day, when Hippolytus is riding with his horses by the sea, a wild white bull will rear up out of the waves and panic the horses, and Hippolytus will be dragged to his death. Thus, from grandfather to father to son, the tradition of bull-killing continues.

And on the island of Naxos, where we left Ariadne languishing and dreaming of her bull-slayer, a Bull-god will step out of her dreams. It is none other than Dionysos, son of Zeus the bull. And the god will undo the wrong that Theseus has done to her, for he will make her his bride and set her by his side in heaven and crown her with a crown of stars and call her Aridela, 'the one visible from afar'. And her beauty still shines out of the northern sky, in the constellation known as the Corona Borealis, the 'crown of the north'.

Thus ends this long and bloody fable of a priestess and a princess and a queen, of a craftsman and a hero and a king … and when one day you too find yourself by the shore gazing seaward, beware of white bulls that arise, bidden or unbidden, from the frothing foam of the wave.

Indra, the chief protagonist of this Hindu myth, is an Aryan warrior sky god who releases the pent-up rains imprisoned by the demon Vritra, and the Brahman who creates the demon is a member of the highest, priestly caste of India. The riddle, which features in this version of the story, is a favourite device in mythology and folklore.

INDRA, VISHNU AND THE DEMON OF DROUGHT

There once was, and there was not, a great and mighty Brahman by the name of Tvashtri, who wished to unseat Indra, God of Storms and Bringer of Rain. So he made himself a son, and infused him with his own power.

Now this son of the Brahman was a sight to behold, for he did not have one head but three. With the first head, he read the Vedas, the holy hymns of praise. With the second head, he ate. And with the third head, he watched the far horizons and saw everything that was in the world, and in piety he exceeded all men.

Up in heaven, Indra had been watching this son of the Brahman. He observed how, through his goodness and restraint, he seemed to grow in power daily, as if he would absorb all the universe, and Indra did not like it one bit. So he looked about him in heaven and chose, from among the damsels there, the most voluptuous, the most seductive, the most sensuous, the ripest and the readiest, and sent them down to tempt the young ascetic.

But no matter how much the damsels fluttered about him and caressed him and wrapped him with the sweet perfumes of their bodies, the son of the Brahman continued to

---

LEFT: A WALL PAINTING OF THE GOD INDRA, DATING FROM THE 7TH–8TH CENTURY AD.

sit, staring out at the far horizons with his cloudless eyes, and refused to be seduced.

This called for more drastic action, Indra could see that plainly, so he wasted no more time but immediately aimed Vajra, his thunderbolt, and struck the son of the Brahman dead. But even in death, the ascetic's power lingered for his body radiated such a light of glory that the whole sky was filled with its splendour. And when Indra ordered a woodcutter to chop off all his three heads, flights of birds rose from the severed necks and the whole sky was filled with their singing.

When Tvashtri heard of the murder of his son, he turned his hand once more to creating, but this time what he made was a gigantic demon, so huge that his head scraped the sky. The demon's name was Vritra, and at the sight of him the clouds held back the rain.

Vritra challenged Indra to a battle and, oh, what a ferocious struggle then followed, and I am glad that you were not there, for the earth shook, and the heavens shuddered, and the seas boiled with the violence of it all. At one point, Vritra seemed to be triumphant for he managed to swallow Indra whole, but when he next opened his mouth, the god shot out again, like a hound from the stocks. In the end, though, Indra had to admit defeat, and fled.

This was an unbearable humiliation for him, and he could not forget. So he consulted Vishnu, who advised that he make peace with his enemy, adding that although there was no weapon now that could kill the demon, perhaps one day there would be.

Vritra agreed to a truce, but imposed terms on the peace.

'Indra must promise,' he said, 'to attack me neither by night nor by day, neither with wood nor stone nor iron, with a weapon that is neither wet nor dry.' The promise was given, and the demon thought himself safe from the god's revenge.

But one day, as Indra was wandering on the seashore, he spied his old enemy not far off and would have attacked him again, but he remembered his promise.

And then he noticed that the sun was setting over the sea and that the dusk was falling, and he realized that it was neither night nor day, and he remembered his promise.

And while he was musing on this, he noticed a strange column of foam rising up out of the sea, and he realized that it was neither of wood, nor stone, nor iron, neither wet nor dry, and he remembered his promise.

'Now is the moment,' said he to himself and, seizing the column of foam he brought it down on the demon's back and split his body in two. And out of the foam came Vishnu, who had been in the weapon all along.

At the death of Vritra, Indra sliced open the bellies of the mountains with his thunderbolt to release the torrents, and broke open the clouds to release the sun and the rain, and the waters flowed over the earth like cattle freed from the pen, and the earth drank as calves suckle from the cow. But Indra could not forget his sin, that he had once killed a Brahman, and he carried the memory with him always.

BELOW: INDRA, SHOWN HERE RIDING AN ELEPHANT, HAD AUTHORITY OVER THE SKY, AND COULD REND THE CLOUDS APART WITH HIS THUNDERBOLT TO RELEASE THE RAIN.

LOVE & MARRIAGE

Devotion, loss and betrayal all feature in these tales of true love, illicit desire and marriages of convenience. They conclude in various ways – in triumph after trials, in justice done, or in the most poignant sorrow for, like true-life love stories, even myths do not always end 'happily ever after'.

CHAPTER SEVEN

Lucius Apuleius set down this classical Graeco-Roman myth in his work 'The Golden Ass', written in about AD 160. Psyche, or 'soul', retains her Greek name, but the god who is here the Romans' Cupid would in Greek have been Eros, the god of 'erotic' love as opposed to agape, non-sexual love. His mother, Venus, was the Greek Aphrodite.

CUPID AND PSYCHE

It wasn't in your time, and it wasn't in my time, but it was in somebody's time – and a very good time it was, to be sure – that there lived a king who had three daughters. Now these three maidens were famed far and wide for their beauty, but of all of them, the youngest – as is the way in such matters – was the most beautiful of all. Her name was Psyche, which means 'soul', and her face was as fair as a spring morning. Indeed, so fair was she that she roused the jealousy of Venus, Goddess of Beauty, who in a fit of vengeful spite sent her son Cupid, the winged God of

Love, to wound the girl with one of his arrows.

Now the arrows of Cupid are the darts of love that pierce the heart and inspire in it undying love for another, and it was Venus's intention that, when the arrow struck Psyche, the unfortunate girl would fall in love with the next beggar or other wretch who came her way.

But even the schemes of the gods sometimes go awry. The very moment Cupid saw Psyche, he was so overcome by her beauty that he wounded himself with the arrow he meant for her, and so it was he, not she, who fell irrevocably in love with the other. As for Psyche, she knew nothing of all of this, for the God of Love had not made himself visible to her.

PSYCHE IS LEFT TO HER FATE
Meanwhile, back in the palace of Psyche's father the king, there was much rejoicing for the marriage of her eldest sister had been cele-

brated, and then that of the second. But for the beautiful Psyche, strangely, no suitors came forward. Her father wondered greatly at this and suspected the hand of the gods in the affair – particularly that of the goddess Venus, whom all knew to have a jealous nature. And so he went to consult the oracle to discover what he should do, but what was his dismay when the oracle uttered the following words:

'Clothe thy daughter as a bride and lead her up the mountainside. Fate will claim her from above as a hawk doth claim the dove.'

None, not even a king, dared to disobey the oracle, so that night Psyche was dressed in the finest bridal robes and led in torchlit procession to the very top of a nearby mountain, where her father bid her a tearful farewell and left her to whatever death awaited her.

Now the poor girl was quite alone in the world. All the torches that had lighted her way up had long since gone, and around her was nothing but darkness. She shivered with fear and wept tears of sorrow. Was this how she was to die, here alone on a mountaintop? Or would some monster of the night swoop down and carry her off to his lair to devour her?

Presently, as she sat there wondering what her fate might be, she felt a warm breeze caress her hair and play with the folds of her gown and she found herself lifted up in the arms of Zephyrus, the West Wind, who carried her to a green valley and deposited her there, on a bank of sweet violets. Lulled by their perfume, she fell into a deep and exhausted sleep.

PSYCHE ENTERS THE PALACE

In the morning, when she awoke and looked around her, she saw before her a magnificent palace. A broad flight of steps led up to it, and its marble columns and walls were carved and painted and decorated in patterns of gold and lapis lazuli and other precious stones, and before it a fountain played.

Charmed at this magical apparition, Psyche entered the palace and began to explore the rooms, each of which was more gorgeous that the last. But nowhere, in all of this magnificence, was there any sign of life, just faint, barely perceptible murmurings as if invisible

beings busied themselves in the empty spaces.

At last, Psyche came to a room where a clear fire burned and a delicious repast was laid. Hungry and tired by now, she sat down and ate her fill, and as she did so, night began to fall. Long, blue shadows stretched their inky fingers through all the rooms of the palace and a cloak of darkness enveloped the world … and in that impenetrable darkness, Psyche felt the air stir and heard a rushing of invisible wings, and the poor girl was terrified. But a soft voice whispered in her ear:

'Be not afraid, for I shall not harm thee. Live with me as my bride, and I shall love and care for thee, and my attendants shall see to thy every wish … only say that thou wilst stay.'

Psyche knew then that she was somehow safe, and her life in the magical palace assumed a pattern as regular as the rising and setting of the sun. Every day was spent in the most pleasant pastimes imaginable and every night her mysterious lover would visit her. But not once did she see his face or his form, for he had warned her:

'Do not ask to look on me, for if thou seest me, I will have to leave thee for ever.'

And Psyche was content with that.

HER SISTERS VISIT PSYCHE

As the days and months passed Psyche began to miss her sisters and wished to see them again, and so it was agreed that Zephyrus would bring them to the palace, just as he had brought Psyche. But before the West Wind set off on his errand, Psyche's lover warned her:

'Pay no heed to what thy sisters tell thee, and do not act on their words or it will go ill for thee and for me.'

BELOW: A PANEL BY JACOPO DEL SELLAIO (1441/2–93) COMBINING VARIOUS EPISODES FROM THE STORY OF PSYCHE AND CUPID.

When the sisters arrived at the palace, they greeted Psyche with much affection and exclaimed in delight at everything she told them, but jealousy at her good fortune gnawed at their hearts, and the blossoming flower of their envy let fall the seeds of doubt.

'Tell us, sister dear,' said they, 'dost thou not find it a matter of the greatest peculiarity that thy beloved has never shown to thee his face? Surely one who hides himself thus must be some hideous, deformed creature – perhaps an ogre that waits his moment to devour thee? Dearest, sweetest sister, would it not be prudent to take a lamp and look on his face while he sleeps, and thus assure thyself as to his true nature?'

The seeds of doubt may take root in the most unlikely of soils, and after her sisters had departed, Psyche pondered long and hard over what they had said, and the more she pondered the more fearful she became. Why had her lover never allowed himself to be seen? And why did he only visit her at night? She determined to find the answer, and that very night, she took an oil lamp and crept over to where he was sleeping and held the lamp so that the light fell on his face … and the face she saw was quite the most exquisite she had ever laid

eyes on, for she was looking on the face of Love itself. Lying there, wrapped in his wings, sleeping a sleep of peace and contentment, was Cupid. It was Cupid who was the Lord of the magical palace. It was Cupid who was her beloved, and she loved him with all her heart.

And she moved the lamp so that she might see him better, but in doing so let fall a drop of the burning-hot oil which landed on Cupid's shoulder, and he woke. He gazed at her for a moment with sad reproach in his eyes. And then, in a flash, he vanished, and so did everything else with him. The palace vanished. The fountain vanished. The green valley vanished. The bank of sweet violets vanished. And there was Psyche, back where she had been at the outset of her adventure, sitting by herself on top of the lonely mountain.

Now began the time of her real trials, as she wandered off into the wide, wide world to seek the one that she had lost.

PSYCHE IS TESTED

Far and farther, over hill and over dale, over mountain and over valley, journeyed Psyche in her quest until at last she arrived at the abode of Venus, the mother of her beloved. Not knowing that the goddess was the real source

of all her sorrows, she appealed to her for help.

'Nothing comes for nothing,' said the goddess tartly. 'If I am to bring thee to my son, thou must first prove thyself worthy by performing a task I have for thee.'

Nearby lay a large pile of seeds, the food of doves and sparrows, composed of wheat, barley, millet and other grains, lying in a jumble together.

'Take these seeds and separate them one by one into piles of their various kinds,' the goddess commanded, 'and have it done by nightfall!'

Psyche sat down, defeated, with her head in her hands, and wept. She had no idea how she was to accomplish the task.

But just then, a small black ant emerged from behind the pile of seeds, followed by a long line of others, and the ants all set to and, with the precision of well-drilled soldiers, made short work of dividing the seeds, wheat with wheat, barley with barley, and so on until all were sorted. By the time the sun had reddened the sky on his way to his rest, all the seeds lay in neat piles.

When Venus saw that the task had been completed, she was not at all pleased.

'This was not done by thine own hand alone,' she said, and the following morning she set Psyche an even harder task.

'Bring me fleece from the golden sheep,' she ordered, pointing to a flock grazing on the opposite bank of a river. Now these sheep were wild and dangerous beasts, with sharp horns and venomous bites, and Psyche had no idea how she was to accomplish the task.

But just then, she heard a reed by the side of river whispering to her, telling her to wait till the sun was low for then the sheeps' ferociousness should be depleted, and she would easily be able to gather fleece shed by them, as much as her arms could hold. And that is exactly what she did.

When Venus saw that the task had been completed, she was not at all pleased.

'This was not done by thine own hand alone,' she said, and the following morning she set Psyche an even harder task.

'Take this crystal vase and fill it from the

CINDERELLA

This tale belongs in the cycle of Cinderella stories, of which there are more than three hundred versions. They all feature a heroine who undergoes a series of trials, either at the domestic hearth or in the wilderness beyond, at the end of which her true worth is revealed and her rightful status achieved, according to the classic story pattern of crisis-initiation-resolution. Anyone who has read 'Beauty and the Beast' will instantly recognize Cupid's magical palace with its semi-absent host, while the task of separating the seeds is identical to that in several versions of Cinderella. In structure, though, the story most closely resembles 'East of the Sun and West of the Moon', the Norwegian wonder tale from the collection of Asbjørnsen and Moe, and its Scottish equivalent, 'The Black Bull of Norroway'.

RIGHT: HER EMBLEMATIC DOVE ON HER ARM, AN IMPERIOUS VENUS COMMANDS THE HAPLESS PSYCHE TO BE BOUND. THE PAINTING IS BY MORITZ VON SCHWIND (1804–71).

Fountain of Forgetfulness,' she commanded.

Now the water of this fateful spring was as freezing as ice, and it lay at the top of a rocky mountain, guarded by two dragons that lived in caves and that never slept. When Psyche arrived at this place, she was dumbstruck with terror. The spring was higher than anyone could possibly climb, and no one could hope to escape the dragons. She had no idea how she would accomplish the task.

But just then, an eagle swooped down, bore off the vase, filled it at the spring, and returned it to Psyche.

When Venus saw that the task had been completed, she was not at all pleased.

'This was not done by thine own hand alone,' she said, and the following morning she set Psyche the hardest task of all.

'Take this box,' she declared, handing her a small casket, 'and go down to the Underworld, to Persephone, Queen of the Dead, and ask her to fill the box with some of her beauty, and then bring it back to me.'

Surely, Psyche thought to herself, this will be the undoing of me, for none can travel to the land of the dead and return. And in her desolation, she climbed to the top of a tall tower, intending to throw herself off it and so end her own life. But the stones of the tower cried out to her.

'Wait, wait!' they called. 'Knowest thou not that there is a path that leads to the Underworld? Follow it and take with thee two coins for Charon and two pieces of bread for Cerberus.'

And that is exactly what she did.

Passing along the dark road to the Underworld, she came at last to the Styx, the River of Hate that flows nine times around the Elysian Fields, where live the dead. And there she gave the first coin to Charon, the ferryman, to ferry her across the river. And on the other bank stood Cerberus, the three-headed watch-dog who guards the entrance to the Underworld, and she gave the first piece of bread as a sop to Cerberus, to let her by. And at last, arrived in the presence of Persephone, she handed her the pyxis, the casket, and the Queen of the Dead filled it with some of her beauty and sealed it.

Psyche returned by the same way as she had come, giving the second piece of bread to Cerberus and the second coin to Charon. Her arduous quest over, she now turned her attentions to the casket. Surely it would do no harm for her to take for herself just a little, no more than a speck, of the beauty it contained, and so she opened the box. But as she did so, she breathed in the invisible vapours that arose from inside, and fell into a deep swoon, that was like unto death.

THE GODS TAKE PITY ON PSYCHE

And there she might have lain for who knows how long had Cupid, now recovered from the wound caused by the burning oil, not observed her sad plight and asked Zeus, Ruler of the Gods, to take pity on her and to bring her to heaven as his wife. It was agreed, and even proud Venus prepared to welcome her, for Psyche's trials were now over.

And so it was that Hermes, Messenger of the Gods, was sent to carry Psyche to Olympus, the home of the gods. And Zeus himself put to her lips the cup containing the elixir of life, and as she sipped the nectar she began to revive and two gossamer wings like those of a butterfly sprouted from her shoul-

ders and she became one with the immortals.

And then there was such a wedding ... and, oh, how I wish you could have been there! The God of Love was married to the girl named Soul, and if all the feasting and merrymaking and rejoicing have not ceased, well ... then they continue still.

BELOW: A lifeless Psyche is borne aloft by Hermes to heaven, reconciliation and immortality, as shown here by Emile Signol (1804–92).

THE BUTTERFLY

The butterfly's wings which Psyche – Soul – acquires at the end of the story are analogous of her transformation from mortal to immortal. The airborne butterfly that emerges from the chrysalis-coffin of the 'dead' earthbound caterpillar is one of mankind's most ancient symbols – going back literally thousands of years – of the rebirth of new life out of the old and, by extension, of the soul's survival after the death of the body.

Taken at face value, this Classical Greek myth tells of the terrible fate meted out by the chaste Artemis to a hunter who dared to look on her naked. The surface narrative, however, masks an older symbolism. The Roman counterpart of Artemis was Diana.

ARTEMIS AND ACTEON

In the woods and mountains of wild Arcadia lived Artemis, virgin Goddess of the Moon and Hunting. Clad in a tunic and hunting boots, armed with a bow and a quiver of arrows, and accompanied by her nymphs and her pack of hounds, she loved nothing so much as the chase. For hours at a time, she and her companions would roam the woods and valleys, tracking the stag or following the roebuck, and when they grew tired, they would stop to refresh themselves by some spring and there, seen only by the silver moon, they would remove their clothes and bathe naked in the crystal waters.

One day, a young huntsman by the name of Acteon was out with his hounds, giving chase to a deer through the very same glades and gorges where Artemis lived. His quarry was fleet of foot and was leading him a merry

ABOVE: THE GODDESS DIANA (ARTEMIS) TAKES HER BATH, IN A PAINTING BY FRANÇOIS BOUCHER (1703–70). *RIGHT*: THE DEATH OF ACTEON, AS SEEN BY TITIAN (C.1489–1576). DIANA, GODDESS OF HUNTING, RELEASES HER ARROW WHILE ACTEON IS TORN TO PIECES BY HIS OWN HOUNDS.

dance, and he soon found himself lost in unfamiliar terrain, in the the valley of Gargaphia. And as he and his hounds picked their way through the trees and the undergrowth, they came to a clearing in the middle of which was a spring – the fountain of Parthenius – and there, in the limpid waters, a group of beautiful young women were dipping themselves and splashing each other and laughing ... but of all these women the most beautiful was the one in the middle. The skin that covered her naked body was milk-pale and radiated light, in her hair she wore a silver crescent, and in perfection she outshone the others as the moon outshines all the stars. The woman Acteon was gazing at was Artemis herself.

Losing all sense of time and place, and forgetting his hounds as they jostled about his legs, Acteon looked on in silent wonder and desire. And although he made no sound to alert her to his presence, the goddess seemed to know that he was there, for she slowly turned and stared straight at him, fixing his face with her steady eyes. It was only a glance, lasting no more than a moment or two, but it felt as if time itself had slowed to a stop.

Under the cool eternity of her gaze, Acteon began to feel his body changing. His arms lengthened and his body thickened; where he once had hands and feet he now had hooves, and on his head two antlers rose. Acteon had been changed into a stag.

The stag bounded over the bushes with Acteon's hounds, hungry to be on the chase, following close behind. The faster the stag ran, the nearer the pack came. It could feel their hot breath on its legs and their barking rang in its ears, and from inside its body, Acteon called out, 'It's me, your master! Do you not know me?' But all the hounds could hear was the cry

SONS AND LOVERS

The thin veneer of this Classical myth veils an older tradition, that of the goddess and her lover by whom she conceives, and who is then killed and 'reborn' from her womb in the form of his own 'son' – his successor and her next lover. In this case the goddess is Artemis and her son-lover is Acteon, and the detail of the myth suggests a ritual rather like those in Crete which mimed the marriage of the solar bull and the lunar cow (see 'Bulls from the Sea', page 152). In this sacred drama, a stag-skin-clad surrogate for the god would have approached the priestess, stand-in for the goddess, similarly clad in a doe skin, to enact the divine union. The priestesses of Artemis, wearing their hunting-dog masks, would then have mimed the dismemberment of the god.

THE RITUAL BATH

The bathing of Artemis also has strong connotions of the ritual bath of the goddess which, according to the Roman historian Tacitus writing of the German tribes in AD 98, only 'men doomed to die' might see.

THE VIRGIN

When reading this myth, one should not be deluded into any coy notions of chastity or virginity. The concept of a 'virgin' goddess goes back to a time when female deities had far greater autonomy and power than under the later, more patriarchal order; they were 'virgins' because they existed and created quite independently of any male principle.

of a stag in terror for its life. And as they closed in for the kill, the beast's dying scream echoed across the hills and down into the valley where Artemis and her maidens were bathing ... and, as the goddess heard it, the shadow of a smile touched her silvery face.

When the hounds had finished with their prey, there was nothing left but a jumble of bones, and so ends the sad story of Acteon who was torn to death by his own dogs, and all for looking on a goddess naked.

This Celtic myth comes from the Second Branch of the the classic collection of Welsh stories known as the 'Mabinogion'. Brân means 'raven', Branwen either 'white raven' or 'white breast', and Gwern 'alder'. Brân is also associated with the alder, for the idea that 'no house could hold him' alludes to the ancient practice of building houses on stakes of alder wood, which does not rot easily, and is therefore 'outside' the house.

THE SORROWS OF BRANWEN

There once was a king called Bendigeidfran, Brân the Blessed, who ruled the Island of the Mighty, and such a giant of a man was he that there was no house in the land big enough to hold him. The king had a sister by the name of Branwen, a brother by the name of Manawydan, and two half-brothers, the sons of his mother, by the names of Nissyen and Evnissyen, who were as different from each other as daylight is different from the blackness of night. Where Nissyen wished for harmony, Evnissyen wished for discord; where Nissyen would make peace, Evnissyen wished to foment strife.

Now it so happened one day, when Brân was holding court at Harlech, overlooking the sea that divided Wales from Ireland, that thirteen magnificent ships were seen approaching, flying sails of silk. On board these ships was the King of Ireland himself, Matholwch, come

LEFT: PRESIDED OVER BY HER GIGANTIC BROTHER BRÂN THE BLESSED, WHOM 'NO HOUSE COULD HOLD', BRANWEN TAKES THE HAND OF MATHOLWCH, HER HUSBAND-TO-BE, AND INNOCENTLY SETS IN MOTION AN IRREVOCABLE CHAIN OF EVENTS.

to ask for Branwen's hand in marriage so that his country and hers might forge an alliance.

Brân welcomed the Irish king and there were discussions and negotiations, and after them a wedding feast, and after the wedding feast, Matholwch lay with Branwen the Beautiful, who had become his wife. And there this tale would have ended, and the princess would have lived happily with her king in the boundless blue ever-after, had it not been for the workings of the evil-hearted Evnissyen.

THE SEED OF SORROW IS SOWN

When Evnissyen discovered that his sister Branwen had been married to Matholwch and that he had not been so much as consulted in the matter, he was filled with rage and a desire for revenge. So he went down to the stables where the horses of Matholwch were quartered, fine Irish steeds every one. And there, in the still hush of night with none around to observe him, he took out his sword and cut the horses' lips from their teeth, slashed their ears from their heads, hacked their tails from their rumps, and sliced their eyelids from their eyes. When his frenzy had abated, not a single horse remained that was not horribly maimed.

News of this outrage soon reached Matholwch, and the king, not knowing who the true culprit was, believed Brân to be responsible. Why he should choose to insult him in this way the king could not understand, for had he not already bestowed on him royal Branwen, his own sister, in marriage? What Matholwch did know, however, was that he had been shamed before everyone, and the only course of action was to leave for Ireland immediately and forget all ideas of alliances with Brân and his kind.

Brân, meanwhile, lost no time in discovering who it was that had really committed the crime, and he hurriedly sent messengers after the departing Irish king.

'Tell him that this outrage was not of my doing, and that I wish to make amends. Tell him that I will give him a new horse for every one that has been injured. Tell him that I will give him a staff of silver as thick as his finger and as high as his head ... tell him that I will

give him a plate of gold as wide as his face ...'

Matholwch was persuaded to return but it still seemed to Brân that he was not entirely appeased, so he decided to offer the Irish king the greatest treasure he had in his possession. He gave him a cauldron. Now this may seem a strange gift for one king to give another, for what use has a monarch, with kitchens full of cooks and turnspits and scullions and servants, for a giant cooking pot, blackened and charred as no doubt it was? But this, of course, was no ordinary stewpot but the magic Cauldron of Regeneration, acquired by Brân from a giant

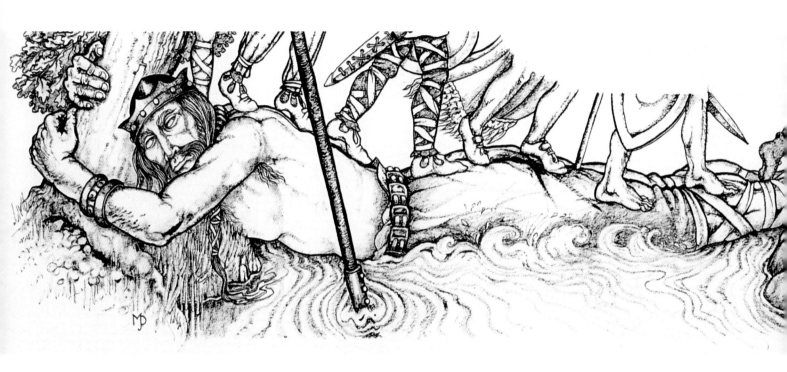

who had brought it out of a lake in Ireland and carried it to the Island of the Mighty, and the wonder of this enchanted receptacle was this: if slain warriors were left to steep in it overnight they would rise the following day, fully restored to life but deprived of the power of speech.

This marvellous gift healed the rift between the two kings, and Matholwch sailed home to Ireland, with Branwen at his side. There was great rejoicing at the arrival of the new queen, and she was showered with so many jewels and brooches and rings that she could, if she had so chosen, rival the very stars of heaven.

THE SEED OF SORROW GROWS

A year passed and Branwen was as happy as a new bride can be, and she bore a son called Gwern, who was sent to live with a foster mother, as was the custom. But behind this semblance of joy an old wound festered, leaching its poison into all the minds of the people of Ireland. That wound was the one caused by Evnissyen when he maimed the king's horses, and the more the people thought about this barbarous act, the more they wanted retribution. Faced with their clamour for revenge, what did King Matholwch do? Take an army against Brân? Demand that Evnissyen be made to atone for his crime? No – what he did was to turn on the one closest at hand, the one it

ABOVE: ON HIS WAY TO AVENGE HIS SISTER'S TREATMENT AT THE HANDS OF THE IRISH KING, BRÂN AND HIS ARMY COME TO A RIVER WITHOUT A BRIDGE. SO HUGE IS BRÂN THAT HE IS ABLE TO FORM A BRIDGE WITH HIS OWN BODY OVER WHICH HIS MEN MAY PASS. THE RIVER MAY POSSIBLY HAVE BEEN THE SHANNON.

was easiest and most convenient to punish. He turned on his own wife, Branwen the Beautiful, Branwen the Blameless, banishing her from the throne and his bed and sending her to work, like a common skivvy, down in the kitchens with the servants. Furthermore, to prevent Brân discovering what had happened to his sister, all trade between Ireland and Wales ceased, and any Welshman coming to Ireland was thrown into prison so that he could not carry the news back home.

All alone in a strange land and with not a friend to help her, Branwen, a noble princess of royal blood, was forced to cook for the court, scrubbing and kneading and chopping and peeling until her soft, white hands were red and rough and sore. This was not her only humiliation, either, for every day the king's butcher would come to the kitchen and slap her across the face with his hands, still bloodied from handling raw meat.

Three years passed in this way, and Branwen's sorrow ran deep into the well of her

soul, and there was not a night when she did not cry herself to sleep. Ignored by the king and ridiculed by the servants, she did in time find one friend, however – a starling that came to perch one day at the kitchen window. Every day after that, the little bird visited her in her loneliness and she would feed it scraps of food, taking care that no one saw for if they knew she had a friend they would chase it away or kill it. The bird became quite tame, and Branwen talked to it longingly about her home across the sea, and told it about her brother, and finally sent the bird off – a small, speckled, winged messenger – with a letter to Brân, telling him all about her humiliation and punishment.

WRONGS ARE RIGHTED

As swift and sure as an arrow, the little bird flew straight to Brân's court at Harlech. When he read the letter his sister had sent him, he called together an army from all the one hundred and fifty-four parts of Wales, and set off to invade Ireland, and it was a terrible sight to see. Such a giant of a man was Brân that he was able to wade across the water by himself, with all his ships full of warriors following in his wake.

As they approached the Irish shore, the first to see them were the swineherds of Matholwch, out tending the king's pigs. In terror, they ran to the palace.

'My lord,' they cried, 'there is a forest on the sea, and in the middle of the forest is a mountain, and there is a ridge on the mountain, and on either side of the ridge there are two lakes! We have seen them with our own eyes, and they are coming this way!'

The court was thrown into confusion and panic. No one could understand what this ominous sight could be. But Branwen, when she was finally asked, knew.

'The forest is the masts of my brother's ships. The mountain is my brother's head. The ridge on the mountain is my brother's nose, and the lakes on either side are his eyes.'

Matholwch was not going to wait to be defeated by a giant and his army, so he and his men fled to the other side of the river that flowed by the palace, destroying the bridge as they did so. The lodestones in the river bed would, they knew, block the passage of any ships that attempted a crossing. But the lack of a bridge was no trouble to Brân, such a giant of a man was he.

'If a man would lead he must be a bridge,' he said, and laid himself down over the river so that his men were able to cross.

When he saw Brân and his army closing in, Matholwch decided to offer peace and told him that he intended to make Gwern, son of Branwen, King of Ireland, in recompense for her suffering. This was all at Branwen's instigation, for she did not wish to see the land ravaged by war.

Brân agreed to peace talks, and because there was no house in the land big enough to hold him, Matholwch ordered a special house built in which the discussions might be held. And it was indeed a special house for when it was done there were pegs all along the walls, and on each peg hung a skin bag, and in each bag an armed warrior was hidden, ready to leap out on Brân and his men.

But it so happened that Evnissyen, who was among Brân's company, came into the great dining hall of the house before the talks began, and was suspicious of the contents of the bags hanging on the walls. He asked an attendant what was in the first one.

'Flour, only flour, my lord,' came the reply.

Evnissyen felt around inside the bag until he found a head, and then he squeezed and squeezed until the brains oozed out of the skull and the eyes popped out of their sockets and the bony shell was crushed like a piece of crumpled paper.

'And what's in this one?' he asked, moving onto the next bag.

'Flour, only flour, my lord,' came the reply as before.

Again Evnissyen reached into the sack and squeezed the head until the brains oozed out, the eyes popped and the skull was crushed, and so it went on until he had killed all the warriors concealed in the bags.

Then all the company gathered and, by the side of a blazing fire, a great feast began, at the end of which Gwern was declared King of Ireland, and peace seemed assured between the two countries. Brân called his nephew to him, and from him Gwern went to Manawydan, and from him to Nissyen.

'Why does the boy not come to me?' complained Evnissyen. Now Evnissyen had never really wished for peace, so when the boy innocently came to him, he picked him up and hurled him into the flames. With a scream of anguish, Branwen tried to throw herself into the blaze after her son, but Brân stopped her and held her between his shoulder and his shield while all around them a terrible battle

broke out between the men of Ireland and the men of the Island of the Mighty. As their warriors fell, the Irish plunged them into the Cauldron of Regeneration – the gift that Brân himself had given them – and they rose alive and ready to fight again. No matter how many of them were slain, the Cauldron brought them back to life, like the hosts of the risen dead on the Day of Judgement.

Looking on, Evnissyen saw his own side being decimated, so he hid himself among the slain Irish warriors and, when he was dropped along with them into the Cauldron, he stretched himself out as far as he could, and the great stewpot split into four pieces, and with it his own heart broke, too, with the effort of the stretching.

ALL SORROW IS FORGOTTEN

And so the Irish were defeated, but of Brân's great army only seven remained: Pryderi, Manawydan, Glinyeu eil Taran, Taliesin, Ynawg, Gruddyeu son of Muryel, and Heilyn son of Gwynn Hen.

Then Brân the Blessed turned to the seven survivors and said:

'Listen carefully: this is what you must do. Cut off my head and carry it home with you to Harlech, where you will spend seven years in feasting. The birds of Rhiannon will sing to you and my head will talk to you, and it will be as pleasant to you in death as I was to you in life. And as long as my head speaks, you will remember no grief. After this time you must take my head to Gwales, to a house with three doors, where you will spend eighty years. And as long as you do not open the door that faces Cornwall, my head will not decay. But if you open that door, you must immediately take my head to the White Hill in London, and bury it

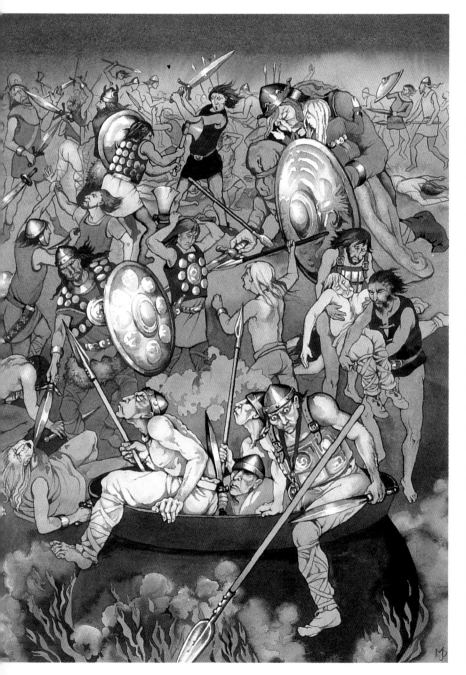

LEFT: THE CAULDRON OF REGENERATION, GIVEN BY BRÂN TO MATHOLWCH, HAD THE POWER TO RESTORE LIFE TO ANY WHO WERE PLUNGED INTO IT. IT WAS ONE OF SEVERAL SIMILAR CAULDRONS FOUND THROUGHOUT INDO-EUROPEAN LORE.

there with my face towards France. Do all these things as I have said, in honour and remembrance of me.'

So the seven survivors cut off Brân's head and carried it with them to Wales, and Branwen with them. As they were crossing the sea, Branwen looked back at Ireland and forward at the Island of the Mighty, and she blamed herself for the conflict between the two countries and for all the men that had died. She thought, too, of the cruelty inflicted on her by Matholwch and of the death of her only son, and the weight of sorrow was more than any one person can bear, and Branwen's heart broke in two, and the seven survivors buried her body in a four-sided grave on the banks of the River Alaw in Wales.

They then journeyed on to Harlech, and all happened just as Brân had said. The three magic birds of the goddess Rhiannon sang to them, and their singing was as sweet as the singing of angels, for they sang of love and of balm for suffering and of the freedom of the heart. And the head of Brân engaged the seven survivors in pleasant conversation, and their hearts and souls were soothed and they forgot all the sorrows and sadness of the world, so that each of the seven years they spent there was as delightful as the one before.

After their allotted time in this place, the survivors made their way to Gwales in Pembrokeshire, where all was just as Brân had said. There was the house with three doors, overlooking the sea. Two doors were open, but the third, which faced Cornwall, was shut. Here they lived, and all the while Brân's head engaged them in pleasant conversation, and their hearts and souls were soothed and they forgot all the sorrows and sadness of the world, so that each of the eighty years they spent there was just as delightful as the one before.

At last, at the end of the eighty years, one of the survivors, Heilyn son of Gwynn Hen, decided to test if what Brân had said about the third door – the one facing Cornwall – was true. He opened it and through it, like a river bursting its banks, came pouring all the despair and anguish of the world that had

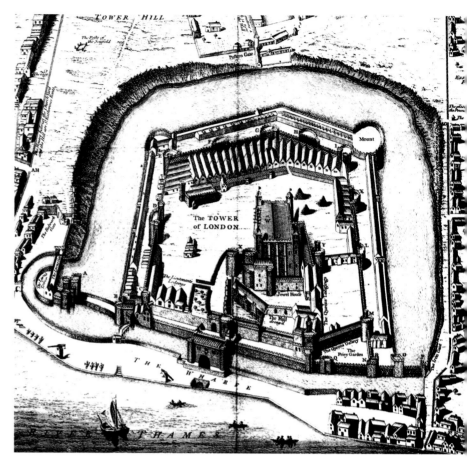

ABOVE: THE WHITE HILL, OR WHITE MOUNT, BENEATH THE TOWER OF LONDON, WHERE BRÂN'S HEAD WAS TRADITIONALLY BURIED. AS IN LIFE, SO IN DEATH – FACING FRANCE, THE HEAD PROTECTED THE PEOPLE OF BRITAIN AGAINST INVASION, JUST AS BRÂN HIMSELF WOULD HAVE DONE WHEN ALIVE.

been kept at bay for so long, and the seven survivors were overcome with grief for all the friends they had lost, all the comrades who had died.

The survivors took the head of Brân to London and buried it on the White Hill with his face looking towards France, just as he had told them to, and all the while that it lay buried there, no plague afflicted the people of Britain, for the island was under the protection of the enchanted head of Bendigeidfran, the head of Brân the Blessed.

And that is the end of the sad story of Branwen the white raven, who wished only for peace and who was blameless of all sin, taken from the old tales that are called the *Mabinogion*.

deceived in this way, Arianrhod again placed a curse on her son – 'He will never get arms till he gets them from me!' said she.

Time passed and Lleu was growing up into a fine and handsome young man. Because of his mother's curse, however, he was not able to bear arms, and this was a great sorrow to him. So, one day, in the guise of bards and tellers of tales, Gwydion and Lleu again approached the castle of Arianrhod. They were welcomed inside and that night Gwydion entertained the company greatly, for he was an accomplished storyteller. But in the morning when he arose, he turned to his magic arts once more and conjured up the image and sound of an army outside the walls of Caer Arianrhod. Arianrhod was deeply frightened.

'Take these weapons to defend the castle for we are under attack,' said she, and gave arms to Gwydion and Lleu.

'My Lady, thou hast armed thy son,' said Gwydion and he and Lleu resumed their proper forms. Furious at being tricked once more, Arianrhod again cursed her son – 'He will never marry until he finds a wife who is not of flesh and blood!' said she.

Now this curse was the most troublesome of all, and was beyond Gwydion's power to overcome, so he went to consult his uncle Math, and together they devised a way to make for Lleu a wife. They gathered all the herbs of the hedgerow, all the flowers of field and forest and then – with much droning of ensorcellments and chanting of Words of Power – fashioned them into the figure of a maiden the like of whom has never been seen before or since for her beauty outshone the fairest morning. And they called the maiden Blodeuwedd, which means Face of Flowers, because she was made from flowers and not from flesh and blood.

From the moment he set eyes on her, Lleu fell deeply in love with Blodeuwedd and they were soon married. But for Lleu the path of true love was soon to give way to a wilderness of despair, for his darling wife, whom he loved almost more than life itself, fell in love with another. His rival's name was Gronwy, and the passion and desire that Blodeuwedd felt for this man far exceeded any feelings she had ever had for Lleu.

And so it was that Blodeuwedd and her lover began to plot to rid themselves of her husband, so that they might be together always. There was one impediment, though, to their plans. Lleu's life, they knew, was undoubtedly guarded by magic, but there must be some way that he could be killed – they would have to discover his secret.

'My dearest one,' said Blodeuwedd to Lleu one day after he had returned from hunting, 'Thou art a great huntsman and warrior, yet I fear for thy life for danger surrounds thee always. Is there no spear nor arrow nor sword

BELOW: BADLY WOUNDED BY GRONWY, LLEU TAKES THE FORM OF AN EAGLE AND GOES INTO HIDING, BUT IS LATER TEMPTED OUT AND HEALED BY HIS OLD FRIEND AND PROTECTOR, GWYDION.

THE RIDDLE

A very common feature of myth and folklore is that of the task or tasks set before particular characters in order that they may prove themselves in some way. The riddle is a very specific type of task, which faced many others besides Blodeuwedd.

ASLOG'S RIDDLE

Challenged by Ragnar Lodbrog to come to him neither riding nor walking, neither naked nor clothed, neither feasting nor fasting, neither attended nor alone, clever Aslog, daughter of the valkyrie Brynhild of Norse myth, solves her lover's riddle by arriving on the back of a goat trailing one foot on the ground, cloaked in no more than a fishing-net and her hair, an onion to her lips, a hound by her side.

DIARMAID'S RIDDLE

In Irish lore, Gráinne, the wife of Fionn Mac Cumhaill who is leader of the warrior band, the Fianna, falls in love with Dairmaid. She places a 'geasa' – a kind of taboo or magical command – upon him to elope with her. Diarmaid is caught in an impossible situation. In an attempt to side-step his destiny (and eventual death through Fionn's cunning), he sets Gráinne an apparently insoluble task: she should appear to him neither by day nor by night, neither clothed nor unclothed, neither on horseback nor on foot, neither alone nor in company. Gráinne seeks the help of a fairy who provides her with garments made from the 'down of the mountainside', which she wears travelling astride a goat in the dusk of the evening.

that can hurt thee? Tell me, is there no way that thou canst be slain?'

Lleu laughed. 'Do not let such sad thoughts darken thy pretty face, ' he replied. 'The only one who can bring about my end must find the answer to a riddle that is beyond answering – he must discover a way to kill me when I am neither indoors nor outdoors, neither walking nor riding, and with a spear that has been a year in the making while all the people are in church on Sundays.'

Blodeuwedd feigned relief. 'Such a riddle as that has no answer,' said she.

But the moment she was alone with Gronwy, she told him what she had discovered. He immediately set to work on the spear and after a year of Sundays it was ready, just as the riddle demanded. Then, somehow, through the

lure of her soft words – although how anyone could be so foolish as to listen to them is beyond all reasoning – Blodeuwedd persuaded Lleu to take the most uncomfortable and contorted bath that anyone has ever taken. A tub was placed for him by the side of a river, under a thatched shelter, with a goat standing by. Then, with Lleu standing perched with one foot in the tub and the other on the goat's back, Gronwy let fly his spear. The spear met its mark and pierced Lleu's side, for – as the riddle stated – he was neither indoors nor outdoors, neither walking nor riding, and so was vulnerable to his attacker's weapon.

With a scream of agony, Lleu turned into an eagle and flew off, and Gronwy took his place at Blodeuwedd's side.

When Gwydion heard what had befallen Lleu, he went in search of him and found him hiding in a tree. With magic verses, he enticed him out, touched him with his staff, and he was changed back from eagle into man, and a pitiful sight he was to behold, too, all skin and bones and wasted flesh and scarred by the wound of Gronwy's spear, and a year he was in the healing.

At last, when Lleu was fully recovered, he gathered together an army and set out, with Gwydion beside him, to avenge himself on Gronwy. But on hearing of Lleu's approach, the latter – self-saving coward that he was – fled the castle with all his men, leaving Blodeuwedd and her women to face Lleu and his army alone. In terror, the women tried to escape across the river but all were drowned, save Blodeuwedd herself.

Perhaps somewhere in his heart, Lleu felt a love for her; perhaps it was through him that her life was spared. For when Gwydion discovered her, cowering by the river bank in fear, he did not kill her but merely touched her lightly with his staff, and she was at once transformed into an owl. And to this day she still haunts the darkness, shunning the light for the shame of the wrong she did. And to this day the Welsh name for the owl is still Blodeuwedd.

So ends this sad and sorry tale of love and hatred, betrayal and revenge, and may we all be wiser for the hearing of it.

This tale was told by the Blackfeet Indians of the plains of northwestern North America. The luminously beautiful imagery that so typifies this and many other Native American stories reveals a sensitivity to nature and a child-like capacity for wonder that are perhaps unparalleled in any other cultural tradition in the world – this is a true 'wonder tale'.

LITTLE STAR AND THE CHIEF'S DAUGHTER

When dawn comes to chase away the darkness and the sky pales from indigo to pearly blue, then, if you look up, you may see a single star, sparkling like a solitary diamond in the broad sweep of the heavens. This is the Star of the Morning, and it heralds the coming of the day.

It was on just such a day as this, when soft mist was still drifting like a veil of gossamer over the earth and the birds were only beginning to stir, that Morning Star looked down and saw an encampment far below him and in the camp he espied a beautiful maiden sleeping. Now although Morning Star was one of the brightest and most beautiful of all the stars, he walked alone in heaven and his heart was lonely. And so it was, as he gazed down on the sleeping girl, that he felt a growing love for her and wished to make her his wife ... and so it was that Soatsaki – for that was her name –

became the bride of Morning Star, and went to live with him in heaven, in the dwelling of his father and mother, the Sun and the Moon.

Now after the passing of nine months, Soatsaki bore a son and his name was called Little Star. As a gift to the new mother, the Moon gave Soatsaki a pick, to help make her work easier in digging up the edible roots that grew below the surface of the soil. There was one condition, however: Soatsaki must on no account, the Moon warned her, use the pick to dig up the turnip that grew near the house of the Spider Man.

But a warning given is a snare laid, and Soatsaki was as curious as any other young woman of spirit and in the end her curiosity overwhelmed her and she went to the house of the Spider Man and did exactly what the Moon said she should not do – she dug up the turnip … and what do you think she saw in the place where the root had been? A hole in heaven itself, through which she could see the earth far below, spread out before her like a giant carpet of every pattern and hue woven by some master weaver. There were the prairies and the herds of buffalo that she remembered so well; there was the river where her people used to fish; there were their tipis with the smoke rising out through the top; and when she saw all these things, her heart was filled with such longing for home that it almost burst.

When the Moon discovered Soatsaki's disobedience, she told her husband the Sun, and the Sun was angry and turned the young woman and her son out of heaven, lowering them to earth wrapped in an elk skin. Down, down, down through the limitless blue air, like a spider on a silken thread, floated Soatsaki, clutching her child to her, until at last they landed on the edge of her people's encampment. And although it was good to be with her own kind once more, Soatsaki knew that she was parted from her husband for ever, and the burden of this sorrow broke her heart and she died, leaving Little Star all alone in the world.

And so it was that Little Star stayed among the Blackfeet, his mother's people, and grew to manhood among them. And he was a fine enough young man except for one thing – his face was disfigured by a scar so that the people, who might have thought differently of him if they had known his true parentage, gave him a cruel name, as ignorant people often will. They nicknamed him Poia, which means 'scarface', and this was a great hindrance to him for when he fell in love with the chief's beautiful daughter and wished to marry her, the proud young woman would not have him, declaring that she could not possibly marry a man with such a scarred face as his.

Hanging his head in shame, Little Star left the camp, left his mother's people, and set out on the long, long road that leads to the west, to the place where the Sun comes to rest in the evening. When at last he reached the shores of the great ocean, he stopped and spent three days there in fasting and prayer. And when he awoke on the morning of the fourth day, a golden pathway had been unrolled across the sea, and Little Star stepped onto it and it bore his weight without sinking and he walked and walked all the way across the wide water to the home of his grandfather, the Sun.

No sooner had he arrived there than he caught sight of his father, Morning Star, in combat with seven monstrous birds that were threatening to overcome him. With all the warrior's skill that he had learned from the Blackfeet, Little Star rushed upon the creatures and killed them, thus saving his father's life.

News of this brave act was soon made known to the Sun so that when Little Star came before him, his grandfather welcomed him as one of his own, and in reward for his bravery gave him three gifts.

As his first gift, the Sun lightly touched Little Star's cheek and the scar that had marked his face all his life was gone, leaving the skin there as velvet-smooth as calf-hide.

As his second gift, the Sun gave him a handful of raven's feathers as a sign of kinship.

As his third gift, the Sun gave him a pipe whose sweet and magical music would win for him the heart of the proud chief's daughter.

The Sun also taught his grandson the ritual of the Sun Dance, and told him to take this knowledge to the Blackfeet people.

Armed with all these gifts, Little Star returned to earth by way of the Wolf Trail – the silver trail of stars that white men call the Milky Way. And when the proud chief's daughter saw Little Star without a blemish on his face, and when she heard him play on his magic pipe music of enchantment, she fell in love with him on the spot. And the two were married and Little Star took his bride up to his grandfather's dwelling, just as his father had done before him, and there they are still to this very day – and how I wish that you could see them – walking arm in arm and step by step across the flower-starred prairie of heaven.

GLOSSARY OF NAMES

AZTEC

Coatlicue – devouring earth goddess, the giver of life and the receiver of it, back into her body. Associated with volcanoes. Her traditional attire included a necklace of skulls and a skirt of serpents or penises of those castrated in her honour.

Coyolxauhqui – goddess of the moon, daughter of Coatlicue, and sister to four hundred brothers, the stars, with whom she colluded in the killing of Coatlicue.

Quetzalcoatl – the feathered serpent god, one of the major deities of the Aztec pantheon. Son of the primordial Ometicuhtli and brother of Tezcatlipoca. A benign deity, he created humankind from bones sprinkled with his blood. Formerly a Toltec god of rain and synthesis of snake and bird, he became in Aztec tradition a god of the wind, the zodiac, the calendar and wisdom. Ruler of the second of the Five Ages of Creation.

Tezcatlipoca – the dark god of the smoking mirror, adopted from the Toltecs. Identified with passages to the supernatural, such as caves, pools, hearth fires and the sun, and was patron of sorcerers who used polished black obsidian mirrors to foretell the future. Complex and capricious, he was the giver of both good fortune and misfortune.

CELTIC

Arianrhod - known as the 'silver wheel', probably an ancient earth goddess, at once mother and virgin. Her sons were Dylan Eil Ton and Lleu Llaw Gyffes. Associated with the constellation Corona Borealis, and with the Greek Ariadne.

Balor – king of the Formorians, pre-Celtic gods of Ireland, traditionally thought of as giants, or sea demons, but probably originally fertility gods demonized by the Celts. Balor's 'evil eye' had the power to destroy an army.

Brân – Bendigeidfran, 'Brân the Blessed', a giant and king of the Island of the Mighty (Britain). Son of the sea god Llyr (identified with Shakespeare's Lear). As Urdawl Ben, the 'Noble Head', his severed head had the power to banish all memories of sorrow and, when buried, prevented invasion. His name also means 'raven'.

Branwen – sister of Brân, the 'white raven'. Possibly a sea goddess, or a goddess of fertility.

Blodeuwedd – wife of Lleu Llaw Gyffes, a woman made out of flowers by the magicians Math and Gwydion.

Cerridwen – British goddess of fertility, also associated with grain and the pig (which link her with the Greek Demeter). Creator of the Cauldron of Inspiration, which conferred poetic inspiration and the power of prophesy.

Dylan Eil Ton – 'Son of the Wave', son of Arianrhod, and the spirit of the sea, the sound of the waves said to be the sound of his dying groan.

Lleu Llaw Gyffes – 'Lion of the Sure Hand', son of Arianrhod and fostered by the magician Gwydion.

Lugh – god of many talents including music, poetry and magic. His attributes were the sling and the spear. Identified with British and Gaulish Lugus.

Taliesin – legendary figure, probably an old British god of poetic inspiration. Confused with the sixth-century poet of the same name.

CHINESE

The August Personage of Jade – Yü-ti, creator god, and second of the supreme triad of Chinese gods, beginning with the Heavenly Master of the First Origin and ending with the Heavenly Master of the Dawn of Jade of the Golden Door. Also known as the August Supreme Emperor of Jade (Yü-huang-shang-ti) or Father Heaven (Lao-t'ien-yeh).

Chih-nii – the Heavenly Spinster, daughter of the August Personage of Jade, spinner of robes made of clouds, and goddess of the star Alpha.

EGYPTIAN

Geb – food of the earth, who was forcibly separated from Nut, the sky.

Horus – principal god associated with the sky and the sun, often depicted as a falcon crowned by the sun.

Isis – wife of brother, Osiris. Great mother goddess, daughter of Geb and Nut.

Nut – goddess of the sky, often shown with her body stretching over the earth.

Osiris – brother and husband of Isis, master of the underworld, first king of Egypt, ruling with his sister, Isis.

Ra – sun god, creator of the other gods and the world in Egyptian mythology. Also known as Re. Identified with Atum.

Set – son of Geb and Nut. God of the desert and associated with the forces of chaos.

GREEK

Athene – one of the most important of the Olympian goddesses, representing war and wisdom. Also known as Pallas Athene. Associated with the Roman Minerva.

Dionysos – god of wine and fertility. Also associated with the bull, the goat and the serpent. His orgiastic female followers were the Maenads. Associated with Bacchus, the Roman god of wine.

Eros – the son of Aphrodite Goddess of Love, often represented as a young boy.

Hercules (Herakles) – said to be the son of Zeus. Most well-known for his great strength, he was worshipped all over Greece.

Odysseus/Ulysses – mythical hero of the *Odyssey* and the *Iliad* which tell the story of the Trojan war and trials endured before arriving home in Ithaca.

Persephone – daughter of Zeus and Demeter, became Queen of the underworld after her abduction by Hades, ruler of the underworld. Associated with Roman Prosperpina.

Perseus – legendary hero and son of Zeus. Famously slew the Gorgon Medusa.

Theseus – legendary hero of Athens, who famously slew the minotaur of Crete. Said to be the son of Poseidon.

INDIAN

Brahma – the Creator, forming a triad with Shiva and Vishnu.

Durgâ – destructive aspect of the consort of Shiva. Other appellations include Uma (light) and Parvati (mountain goddess).

Indra – Hindu god of storms and bringer of rain. Often shown riding an elephant.

Krishna – eighth of the ten avatars (incarnations) of Vishnu.

Lakshmi – Goddess of Beauty and Good Fortune. Associated with Aphrodite in Greek mythology, rose from the sea.

Shiva – the Destroyer in Hindu mythology. Often represented as white with a blue throat.

Vishnu – the Preserver, consort of Lakshmi.

JAPANESE

Amaterasu – the sun goddess, from whom the royal family claim descent.

Izanagi – known as the 'male who invites'. Creator of the world with his sister – wife, Izanami.

Izanami – 'the female who invites'. Creator of the world, with her brother – husband, Izanagi.

Susano-Wo – god of storms, born from the nose of Izanagi.

NATIVE AMERICAN

Aataensic – a deity of the Iroquois, Algonquin and Huron Indians whose fall from heaven caused the creation of the earth.

Michabo – Algonquin creator god, and giver of the arts of hunting and making fishing nets. Also ruler of the east wind and the lightning, mist and cloud being the smoke from his pipe. Lives on an island in Lake Superior or somewhere to the east in the far ocean. Also known as the 'Great Hare', which title is a corruption of an aboriginal root meaning 'the light of dawn'.

Mondamin – corn spirit of the Ojibwe Indians.

Tirawa – the supreme god of the Pawnee Indians of the Plains.

NORSE

Balder – son of Odin and Frigg, god of light.

Bor – son of Buri, father of Odin, Vili and Ve.

Freya – goddess of love and beauty.

Idun – goddess who possessed the apples which provide eternal youth.

Loki – the trickster of the Norse pantheon, a malicious and crafty god.

Odin – supreme Norse god known as the 'allfather'. God of magic, poetry and battle. With his brothers Vili and Ve created the world.

Thor – son of Odin, and god of thunder.

POLYNESIAN

Maui – god 'of a thousand tricks' who was always up to mischief of some sort, allying himself with mankind against the gods. He made the islands of the Pacific, gave mankind fire, made more space between heaven and earth, and contrived a longer day, but his bid for immortality caused his death. According to Hawaiian tradition, he was killed because people tired of his tricks, and it was his blood that turned shrimp red and coloured the rainbow.

Old Spider – creator of the world in a localized myth from the island of Nauru.

SUMERO-BABYLONIAN

Enkidu – also known as Eabani, the wild man created from mud to be a friend to Gilgamesh.

Erishkigal – dark goddess of the underworld, twin sister to Ishtar.

Gilgamesh – semi-mythical Mesopotamian king who almost became immortal.

Ishtar – mother goddess embracing the spheres of fertility, love and war. Twin sister to Erishkigal, underworld goddess. Identified with her Sumerian forerunner Inanna. Her lover was Tammuz, counterpart to Inanna's Dumuzi.

Marduk – Babylonian god who killed Tiamat to become king of the gods and creator of mankind.

Tiamat – mother goddess and personification of the primordial ocean, from whose lifeless body, according to Babylonian myth, the world was formed.

Tammuz – lover of the goddess Ishtar, and the embodiment of the corn.

Uta-napishtim – forerunner of Noah, granted immortality after surviving a great flood and living in peace with his wife on a blessed island across the Waters of Death. Also known as Ziusudra.

BIBLIOGRAPHY

Baring, A. and Cashford, J., *The Myth of the Goddess: Evolution of an Image.* Harmondsworth, 1991.

Bulfinch, T., *Bulfinch's Mythology.* London, 1963.

Campbell, J., *The Masks of God,* vols i-iv. New York, 1959.

Crossley-Holland, K., *The Norse Myths.* London, 1980.

Crossley-Holland, K. and Thomas, G., *Tales from the Mabinogion.* London, 1984.

Eliade, M., *Shamanism.* Harmondsworth, 1989.

Farrar, F. A., *Old Greek Nature Stories.* London, 1914.

Ferguson, D., *The Magickal Year.* London, 1996.

Frazer, Sir J., *The Golden Bough.* London 1890–1915.

Gimbutas, M., *The Goddesses and Gods of Old Europe.* London, 1982.

The Language of the Goddess. San Francisco, 1989.

Guirand, F. (ed), *New Larousse Encyclopedia of Mythology.* London, 1959.

Hallam, E. (ed), *Gods and Goddesses.* London, 1996.

Hyde, L. Stoughton., *Favourite Greek Myths.* London, 1911.

Jordan, M., *Myths of the World.* London, 1993.

MacCulloch, J. A., *The Religion of the Ancient Celts.* Edinburgh, 1911.

Orbell, M., *The Illustrated Encyclopedia of Maori Myth and Legend.* Christchurch, 1996.

Rees, A. and Rees, B., *Celtic Heritage.* London, 1961.

Smith, W. Ramsay, *Aborigine Myths and Legends,* 1930.

Spence, L., *North American Indians: Myths and Legends.* London, 1994.

The Myths of Ancient Egypt (1915), re-published as *The Illustrated Guide to Egyptian Mythology.* London, 1996.

Taylor, C., *North American Indians.* Bristol, 1997.

Williamson, R., *The Craneskin Bag.* Edinburgh, 1989.

Walker, B. G., *The Woman's Dictionary of Symbols and Sacred Objects.* San Francisco, 1988.

The Woman's Encyclopedia of Myths and Secrets. San Francisco, 1983.

INDEX

Page numbers in *italics* refer to picture captions.

Aataensic 32–3
Aboriginals, Australian 50–1, *50*, 59
Acheron 98
Acrisius 137, 138, 141
Acteon 168–9, *168*
Adjidaumo 125
Admete 149
Adonis 115
Aegeus 155–7
Aeolus, King 64, *65*
Aesir, the 23, 92–3, 101
Afagddu 102–3
Alcestis, Queen 149
Alcmene 142–3
alder 170
Alessandro, Allori *15*
Alfheim 23
Algonquin 32, 34–5
allegory 12, 19
almonds 11, 115
Alpheus river 147
Alsaeids 130
Amairgen 102
Amaterasu 27, 48–9, *48, 49*
Amazons 149
ambrosia 121
Ame-No-Minaka-Nushi-No-Kami 26
Ame-No-Uzume 49
Ampelos 128–9
Amphitrite 155
Amphitryon 142, 143
Amrita 36–7
Ananta the Infinite *36*, 83
Androgeus 155
Andromeda 141
Angas, George French 57
Angurboda 151
animals
    anthropomorphic 7
    assuming identity of 66
    supporting the earth 33, *33*
    talking 7, 62–3
    see also individual animals

animism 14–15
Annwn 151
Anshar 18–19
anthropomorphic animals 7
Anu 18–19, 80
Anubis 89, 119, 151
Aoraki 58
Aphrodite (Venus) *10*, 11, 115, *157*
    Cupid and Psyche 162–7, *166*
Apis 153, 154
apocalypse 44–5
Apollo 65, 96
apple trees 12
apples 75
    Avalon (apple land) 75
    Golden Apples of Idun 72–5, *73*
    Golden Apples of Immortality 75, 140, *147*, 150–1
apricots 122
Apsu 18
Apsuras, the 37
Apuleius, Lucius 162
Arachne 106–7, *107*
Araiteuru 58
Arawn 151
Arcadia 168–9
archetypes 9–12
Ares 149
Argo 97
Argus Panoptes 153
Ariadne *12*, 153, 155–7, *157*, 176
Arianrhod 176–8, *176*
Aridela 157
Armenian mythology 15
Artemis (Diana) 65, 147, 168–9, *168*
Arthur 75
Aruru 77
Aryans 12–13, 53
Asbjørnsen and Moe 166
Asgard 23, 38, 41, 44–5, 73–5, 100
ash trees 22–3, 100
Ashurbanipal 76

Ask 22–3
Aslog's riddle 179
Assyrian mythology *see* Babylonian and Assyrian mythology
Astarte 85, 115, 118–19
Asushu-Namir 114
Asvattha tree 23
Athene 8, 106–7, *106, 107*, *138*, 139–40, *140*, 141, *147*
Athens 152, 155, 156–7
Atlas *147*, 150–1
atonement 144
Attis 9, 11, 12, 115
Atum 29
Atum-Ra 28–9
Audubon, John James *61*
Audumla 21
Augeias, Stables of 147
August Personage of Jade 62–3
Aukelenuiaiku 59
Auloniads 130
Avalon (apple land) 75
axis mundi (world tree) 23, *23*, 45
Aztec mythology 9, 11, *11*, 35, *48*
    the elements 67
    Evening Star 54–5, *54, 55*
    night and day 52–3

Babylonian and Assyrian mythology 12, 13–14, 18–19, *18*, 35, 51, *73*
    creation myth 18–19, *18, 19*
    Gilgamesh 76–83, *76, 77, 78, 80*
    Ishtar and Tammuz 112–15, *112, 113, 114, 115*
Bacchus *see* Dionysos
Balder 38–43, *41, 42*, 44, 45
Balen, Hendrick van *153*
Ballad of True Thomas 75
Balor 136–7
banshee 109

baptism 125
baths, ritual 169
battles
    Durgâ and Mahisa 134–5, *134, 135*
    Mag Tuireadh 137
Baugi 94–5
beans 122
beansídhe 109
Beauty and the Beast 166
beavers 32–3, *32*
Beltane 104, *104*
Bemahgut 125
Bendigeidfran 170, 175
Bestla 21
Bible
    Genesis 19
    Jonah and the Whale 37, 51
    Leviathan 25
    Noah and the Deluge 35
    Virgin Mary 11–12
Bifröst 23, 39, 45, 59, 74, *74, 75*
birds 32-3, 49, 87, 175
    Birds of Stymphalus 146
    Sorrows of Branwen *171*, 173
birth
    lunar phases 51
    miraculous conception 10–11, 52–3, 115, 177
    Talicsin of the Shining Brow 102–5
    Triple Goddess 14
Black Bull of Norroway 166
Blackfeet 180–1
Blodeuwedd 177–9, *177*
boars 115, 119
    Boar of Erymanthus 146, *148*
Bodn 93–5
Bor 21
Boreas 64
Boucher, François *168*
Brahma 14, *18*, 135
Brahmans 14, 158–9
Brân the Blessed 96, 170–5, *170, 172*

Branwen 170–5, *170, 171*
Brazilian mythology 59
bridge of heaven 39, 45, 59, 74, *74*
Brisingamen *74*
Bronze Age cultures 13
brothers 9, *20*, 21, 24, 54–5, 93, 142, 170
see also siblings
Buddhism 8
bulls 77, 80, *80*, 114, 152–7
  Black Bull of Norroway 166
  Bull of Crete 147–8, *148*, 152–7
  bull dancing 156
  Dionysos and the Vine 128–9
  Minotaur *12, 134*, 152, *154*
  ritual sacrifice 156
  solar bull 153, 156, 169
Buri 21
butterflies 167

Caer Arianrhod 176, 177–8
Caer Dathyl 176–7
Calliope 96
Canaanite mythology 85
Caravaggio, Michelangelo *138*
castration 115
Catlin, George *180*
cats 73
cattle 21, 37, 62–3, *62*, 65, 73
  Cattle of Geryon 149–50
  lunar cow 153, 156, 169
  solar bull 153, 156, 169
  see also bulls; cows
Caucasus, Mount 69
cauldrons 37, 93, *93, 102*
  Cauldron of Inspiration 102–5, *103*
  Cauldron of Regeneration 171–4, *174*
Celeus, King 121
Celtic mythology 11, 13, 31, 72
  Avalon (apple land) 75
  fairy stories 57
  Hounds of Annwn 151
  Lleu Llaw Gyffes and Blodeuwedd 177–9
  Lugh 136–7

  Sorrows of Branwen 170–5
  Taliesin of the Shining Brow 102–5
  see also Irish mythology; Welsh mythology
centaurs 13, 151
Centzon-Huitznahuas 52–3
Cerberus 13, 98–9, *123*, 148, 151, 166-7
Ceres *see* Demeter
Cerridwen 11, 102–3, *103*
Ceryneia, Hind of 146–7, *148*
Ceto *139*
chakras 83
chameleons 84–5
Ch'ang-o 85
chaos (pre-creation) 26, 28
chariots 6, 19, 22, *120*
Charon 98–9, 166–7
Chih-nii 62–3
Chinese mythology 59
  Cowherd and the Heavenly Spinner 62–3, *63*
  Moon's guardian 85
Christ 9, 10, 12, 127
  resurrection 51
Christianity 8, 9, 127
  Christmas Day 53
  Easter 85, 115
  Holy Communion 127
  Virgin Mary 10–11
Christmas Day 53
Cian 136
Cinderella 166
cloaks 61, 72, 75
clouds 21, 65, 89, 152
Coatlicue 11, 52–3, *53*
cocks 45, 49
Cocytus 98
Codex Regius 100
Colhuacan 35
colours
  black 14, 54
  blue 54
  red 14, 54
  white 14
conception, miraculous 10–12, 52–3, 115, 177
conquering heroes 53
corn and corn gods 54, 112, 127
  Lammas 136
  see also crops; fertility

Corona Borealis 157, *157*, 176
Cortona, Pietro da *148*
Cowherd and the Heavenly Spinner, the 62–3, *63*
cows 21, 37
  lunar cow 153, 156, 169
Coxcoxtli 35
Coyolxauhqui 52–3, *52*
coyotes 89
  Coyote and the Theft of Fire 66–7
creation myths 7, 16–33
  Babylonian 18–19, *18, 19*
  Egyptian 28–9, *28, 29*
  Genesis 19
  Indian 36–7, *37*
  Japanese 26–7, *26, 27*
  matriarchy and patriarchy 11–12, 19, 25
  Message of Unkulunkulu 84
  Native American 32–5, *32, 33*
  Norse 20–3, *20, 22, 23*, 38–45
  Polynesian 24–5, *24, 25*, 30–1, *30*
Creator 14
creator-destroyer goddess 87
Creon, King 143
Crete, Bull of 147–8, *148*, 152–7
crops 110–31
  Demeter and Persephone 120–3, *120, 121, 122, 123*
  Ishtar and Tammuz 112–15, *112, 113, 114, 115*
  Isis and Osiris 116–19, *116, 117, 118, 119*
  Mondamin and the Indian Corn 124–7, *126*
  see also corn and corn gods; fertility
crossroads *143*
crows 51
Cú Chulainn 11, 13
Cuban mythology 59
cultural change, myths as record of 12
Cupid *see* Eros

Cyanean Rocks 58
Cybele 11, 115

Daedalos 155–6
Dagda 37
Damballah 59
Danaë 138–9, 141
Danaids 98
Danann 136
darkness, *Sol Invictus* 13
dawn 35, 49
Day 22, 52–3, 65
days of the year 29
De Morgan, Evelyn *121*
death 8, 13–14
  banshee 109
  Death of Balder the Beautiful 38–43, *41, 42*
  dogs and wolves 89, 151
  Hades 98–9, *99*, 122–3, *123*, 151
  Irkalla 113–15
  life after 8, 23, 27, 28, 87
  Lightning and the Sack of Storms 88–9
  lunar phases 51
  Maui and the Waters of Life 86–7, *86*
  Odin 100–1
  Orpheus and Eurydice 92, 96–9, *96, 98, 99*
  psychopomps 151
  Triple Goddess 14
  see also immortality, quest for; resurrection and rebirth; underworld
Dechtire 11
Deianeira 151
Delville, Jean 97
Demeter 14, 120–3, *121, 122*
demons 134–5, 158–9
Destroyer 14
Dhanvantari 37
Dian Cécht 136
Diana *see* Artemis
Diarmaid's riddle 179
Dicksee, Sir Frank *41*
Dictys 138
Diomedes, Mares of 148–9, *148*
Dionysos (Bacchus) *12*, 127, 128–9, *128, 129*, 153, 157, *157*
dogs 89, 151
  Artemis and Acteon 168–9, *168*

Cerberus *13*, 98–9, *123, 148*, 151, 166–7
  hounds of Annwn 151
  Moon-dogs 151
dragons 19, 100, 150, 166
drought, demon of 158–9
Dryads 130
duality 9, 13–14
Dumuzi 12, 112, 115
Durgâ 14, 134–5, *134, 135*
dwarves 22–3, *22*, 93–4
Dylan Eil Ton 177

Ea 18–19, 114–15
eagles 68, 69, 73–5, 95, 100, 166, 179
earth 13, 67
  animal supporting 33, *33*
  axis mundi (world tree) 23, *23*, 45
  creation *see* creation myths
  four corners 19, 22, *22*
  gender 28
Earth Mother 35, 120–3, 150
East 22, 54, 64, 89
East of the Sun and West of the Moon 166
Easter 85, 115
Echo 130–1, *131*
edimmu 113
Egyptian mythology 12, 83, 85, 89, 154
  corn god 127
  creation myth 28–9, *28, 29*
  Isis and Osiris 116–19, *116, 117, 118, 119*
  pantheon 29
elements, the 67
elephants *33*
Eleusis 121
elm trees 23
Elphin 104–5
elves 23, 75
Elysian Fields 166
Embla 22–3
enchantment 95
Enkidu 77–81, *78*
Enlil 79
Eoestre 85
Epaphus 154
Erishkigal 15, 113–15
Eros (Cupid) *152, 162, 163, 164*

Erymanthus, Boar of 146, *148*
Ethniu 136
Etruscans 69, *139*
Europa *152*, 153, *153*, 154
Europe 154
Eurus 64
Euryale 139, 141
Eurydice 97–9, *98, 99*
Eurystheus 13, 143, 144–51
Evnissyen 170–4

fairies 57–9, 75, 108–9
  fairy fruit 75
  fairy godmothers 109
  fairy wives 57–9, 108–9
falcons 75, *117*
fall of man 76
fate
  Perseus and Acrisius 138–41
  Thread of Destiny 30, 31
  Well of Fate and the Norns 23, 100
  Wheel of Fortune 31
Fates 31, 75, 109
Father-Heaven 62–3
fathers and sons 129, 137
feathers 11, 52, 61, 181
Fenrir 44, 45
fertility 110–31
  ritual sacrifice 115, 156
  sacred marriage 156
  symbols 122
  see also corn and corn gods; crops
Festival of the First Fruits 48–9
Fianna 179
figs 122
Fimbulven 44
Fionn Mac Cumhaill 179
fire 27, 67, 118–19, 121
  Coyote and the Theft of Fire 66–7
  Land of Fire 20–1, 45
  Prometheus and the Theft of Fire 68–9, *68, 69*
fish and fishing 24–5, 32–3, 61, 104–5
Fisher, Harrison *124*
Fjalar 45, 93–4
Flier 19
floods 34–5, 116, 119
Flora 176

folk tales 7, 8
Fomoire 136–7
fonts 37
forests 58
Fountain of Forgetfulness 166
Fountain of Parthenius 168
Fountain of Youth 37
four corners of Earth 19, 22, *22*
Freya 73, *74*, 75
Freyr 101
Frigg 38–40
fruit
  fairy 75
  forbidden 122
  Fruits of Immortality and All-Knowing 83
  magic 72–5
  as symbols of fertility 122
  vine 128–9
  see also apples
funeral dirges 114
Furies 143
Futo-Tama 49

gadflies 129, 153
Gaea 35, 150
Galar 93–4
Garden of Eden 12, 83
Gargaphia 168
geasa 179
Geb 28–9, *28, 29*
Gemmyo, Empress 26
Genesis 19
Gensho, Emperor 26
Geryon, Cattle of 149–50
giants 20, 21–3, 41, 45, 74, 93–4, 150–1, 153, 170–5
Gilfaethwy 176
Gilgamesh 76–83, *76, 77, 78, 80*
Gilling 93–4
Gimbutas, Marija 13
Ginnungagap 20–1
Girdle of Hippolyte 149
Gjall 45
Gladsheim 40
Glinyeu eil Taran 174
godmothers, fairy 109
gods and goddesses 7, 9
  dual personalities 13–14
  matriarchy and patriarchy 11–12, 13, 25
  nature of divinity 8

saviour gods 9
Goewin 176
Golden Apples of Idun 72–5, *73*
Golden Apples of Immortality 140, *147*, 150–1
Golden Ass, The 162
good and evil, duality 9
Gorgons, the 14, 138–41, *138, 139, 140, 141*
Graeae, the *139*, 140
Gráinne 179
Great Mother *see* Mother Goddess
Greek mythology 8, 12, *12*, 13, *13*, 14, *14*, 15, 31, 35
  Aphrodite and Adonis 115
  Apples of the Hesperides 75
  Arachne the Spinner 106–7, *107*
  Artemis and Acteon 168–9, *168*
  Dionysos *12*, 127, 128–9, *128, 129*
  Echo and Narcissus 130–1, *130, 131*
  Hercules (Herakles) 13, *13*, 69, *69*, 142–51, *142, 143*
  How Winter Came into the World 120–3
  moving mountains 58
  oracles 138, 143, 144, 163
  Orpheus 92, 96–9, *96, 97, 98, 99*
  Perseus and the Gorgon 13, 137, 138–41, *138, 139, 140, 141*
  Prometheus and the Theft of Fire 68–9, *68, 69*
  rainbow 59
  Theseus and the Minotaur 152
  Ulysses *15*, 64–5, *64*
Gronwy 178–9
Gruddyeu son of Muryel 174
Guardian of the Inn 81
Guerard, Eugen von 59
Guinevere 59
Gullinkami the Golden Comb 45

Gunderstrup cauldron *102*
Gunnlöd 94–5
Gwaelod 104
Gwales 174, 175
Gwern 170, 172–4
Gwion Bach 11, 103
Gwyddno Garanhir, King 104, *105*
Gwydion 176–8
Gypsy mythology 75

Hades 98–9, *99*, *120*, 121–3, *123*, 151
Haggarty, Ben 8
hair bridge 59
Haitian mythology 59
hallucinatory flight 72
Hanged Man 100–1, *100*
hares 7, *85*
   Great Hare (Michabo) 35
   Message of Unkulunkulu 84–5
Harlech 174
harvest festivals 48–9, 136
Hathor 85
Hati 22, 45
Havamal 100
Hawaiki 58
heaven *see* bridge of heaven; sky
Hebrus 99
Heilyn son of Gwynn Hen 174, 175
Heimdall 45
Heintz, Joseph *120*
Hel 23, 39, 42–3, 151
Helios 149
Hephaestos 69
Hera 12, 75, 130–1, 142–3, 149, 152–3
Heraion 152
Hercules (Herakles) 13, *13*, 69, *69*, 142–3, *142*, *143*
   Twelve Labours *13*, 144–51, *144*, *145*, *147*
Hermes 139–40, 151, 153, 167, *167*
Hermod 42–3
heroes
   conquering 53
   solar 53
Hesiod
   Theogony 68
Hesperides 12, 75, 140, 150–1
Hi-No-Kagu-Tsuchi 27

Hiawatha 124, *124*, *126*
Hind of Ceryneia 146–7, *148*
Hinduism 7, *10*, 11, 14, *18*, 23, 83, 134–5, 151, 158–9
Hine-nui-te-po 87
Hine-pukohu-rangi 57–9
Hine-rehia 108–9
Hine-wai 57
Hipo 58
Hippodameia 139
Hippolyte, Girdle of 149
Hippolytus 153, 157
Hiroshige 27
historical figures 7
   Gilgamesh 76–83, *76*, *77*, *78*, *80*
history, myth as 7, 12–14
Hnitbjorg 94–5
Hoard-thoughts 49
Höd 39–41, *40*, 45
Hoddmimir's Wood 45
Holle, Mother 109
Holy Communion 127
Homer
   Odyssey 64
Honir 73
horses 13, 19, 39, *39*, 41
   Mares of Diomedes 148–9, *148*
   Pegasus 141
   Sorrows of Branwen 171
Horus 29, 119, *119*
Hrym 45
Huginn 100
Huitzilopochtli 52–3
hurricanes 19
Hvergelmir 20–1, 23, 100
Hydra of Lerna 145–6, *145*, *148*
hydromel 94–5
Hylaeorae 130
Hyrrokin 41

Iaptos 68
Ice, Land of 20–1
Idun 72–5, *73*
Imbolc *104*
immortality, quest for 70–89, 118–19, 121
   Cauldron of Regeneration 171–4, *174*
   Fountain of Youth 37
   Fruits of Immortality and All-Knowing 83
   Gilgamesh 76–83, *76*,

77, *78*, *80*
   Golden Apples of Idun 72–5, *73*
   Golden Apples of Immortality 140, *147*, 150–1
   Lightning and the Sack of Storms 88–9
   Maui and the Waters of Life 86–7, *86*
   Message of Unkulunkulu 84–5
   Psyche 167, *167*
   see also life after death; resurrection and rebirth
Inanna 12, 112
Indian mythology 12, 14, *18*
   creation myth 36–7, *37*
   Durgâ and the Demon 134–5, *134*, *135*
   Indra, Vishnu and the Demon of Drought 158–9
   see also Buddhism; Hinduism
Indo-European tradition 12–13, *12*, *13*, 14, 18, 20, 53, *93*
Indra 37, 158–9, *158*, *159*
initiation rites 7, 125, 151, 166
Io 152–4
Iolaus 145, *145*
Ionian Sea 153
Iphicles 142, 143
Iris 59, 122
Irish mythology 7, 8, 11, 12, 37, 75, 95, 102, 109, 179
   Lugh 11, 136–7, 176
   Tuatha Dé Danann 136–7
   see also Celtic mythology
Irkalla 113–15
Iroquois 32–3
Ishtar 11, 12, 13–14, 79–81, *79*, *80*, 112–15, *112*, *113*, *114*, *115*
   seven veils 79, 114, *114*
Isis 11, 12, 29, 116–19, *117*, *119*
Islam 8, 23
Island of the Blessed 81
Izanagi 26–7, *26*, *27*, 48
Izanami 26–7, *26*, 48

Jaganmata 14
Japanese mythology
   creation myth 26–7, *26*, *27*
   Sun in Hiding 48–9, *48*, *49*
Jason 58, 97
Jata-Kagami 49
Jehovah (Yahweh) 11, 19, 25, 115
Jindaiki 26
Jonah and the Whale 37, 51
Jormungand 22, 45
Jotunheim 23, 74–5, 100
Judaism 9

Kaitangata 58
Kali *53*, 134
Kali Ma 14
Kami-Musubi-No-Kami 26
Karanga-roa 108
Ke-ig-nish-im-o-win 124–7
Khumbaba 79
King of the Bean 122
Kingu 19
Kirk, M.L. *126*
Kishar 18
Klimt, Gustav *106*
Knossos 152, 154–5
Koch, Max 6
Kojiki 26
Kore 14, 120–3
Krishna 135
Kundalini 83
Kurgans 13
Kvasir 93–4

labyrinth *154*, 155–6, *155*
Ladon 75, 150
Laius 137
Lakhamu 18
Lakhmu 18
Lakshmi *10*, 11, 14, 36–7
Lammas 136
Launcelot 59
legends 7, 8
Lemnos 69
Lerna, Hydra of 145–6, *145*, *148*
Lesbos 99
Lethe 98
Leviathan 25
Lif 45
life 13–14
   lunar phases 51
   Triple Goddess 14

life after death 8, 23, 27, 28, 87
   see also immortality, quest for; underworld
Lifihrasir 45
lightning 6, 13, 18–19, 45, 53, 68, 89
   Lightning and the Sack of Storms 88–9
Liknites 127
Lion of Nemea *144*, 145, *148*
Little Star 180–1
Lleu Llaw Gyffes *176*, 177–9, *178*
Loki 24, *38*, 40–1, *40*, 44–5, 73-5
London, White Hill (White Mount) 174, 175, *175*
Longfellow, Henry Wadsworth
   The Song of Hiawatha 124, *124*
lotus 7
Lugh 11, 136–7, 176
Lughnasadh *104*, 136
Lycett, Joseph *50*

Mabinogion 102, 170, 175, 176
mace 7
Maelgan 105
Maenads 99, 128
magic 90–109
Mahisa 134–5, *134*, *135*
Mahnomonee 125
man, creation 19, *19*, 21–3, 32–3, 89
mana 58
Manawydan 170, 174
Mandara, Mount 36–7
Maori mythology 15, 59
   magic mountains 58, *109*
   Maui and the Waters of Life 86–7, *86*
   Mist and Rainbow 56–9
   Secret of Weaving 108–9, *108*
   see also Polynesian mythology
Marduk 12, 18–19, *19*
Mares of Diomedes 148–9, *148*
marriage, sacred 152–7, 169
Mary *see* Virgin Mary

Maskenozha 125
Master of the Campana Cassoni *157*
Matakaea 58
Math 176–8
Matholwch 170–5, *170*
matriarchal mythology 11–12, 19, 25
Maui 24–5, *24*, 86–7, *86*
May Eve 104, *104*
Mayan mythology 31
mayfly 11
Mead of All-Knowing 92–5
Medusa *14*, 138–41, *138*, *140*
Meenahga 125
Megara 143
Mehen the Enveloper 83
Melcanthus 117–18
metamorphosis 6, 15, 54, 58, 103, 169
Metaneira 121
Michabo and the Flood 34–5
Midgard 22–3, 39, 44–5, 73–4, 75, 95
Milk, Churning of the Ocean of 36–7, *37*
Milky Way 89, 181
Mimir 23, 100
Minoans 153
Minos 148, 153, 154–6
Minotaur *12*, *134*, 152, 154–6, *154*, *155*
mirrors 49, 54
   see also reflections
Mist and Rainbow, The 56–9
mistletoe 38, 40, *40*
Mithra 13, 53
Mixcoatl 52
Mixtecs 55
Mjölnir 41, *42*
Moaning-river 27
Mohini 37
Mondamin and the Indian Corn 124–7, *126*
monsters 18–19, 25, 79
Montezuma 54
Moon 13
   Aztec mythology 52–3
   creation 22, 31, 37, 84
   disappearing 50–1, *50*
   Egyptian mythology 29
   eight-yearly cycle 153, 156

   as gateway to afterworld 151
   god 27, *27*
   hare as guardian 85
   ladder to the 7–8
   and Little Star 180–1
   lunar cow 153, 156, 169
   lunar division of the year 104
   Maui and the Waters of Life 86–7
   Message of Unkulunkulu 84–5
   Moon-dogs 151
   Native American mythology 89
   phases 51
   Ragnarok 45
Morgan le Fay 75
Morning Star 180–1
Morrígan 75
Mother Goddess 10, 11–12, *11*, 13, 25, 31, 32, 35, 37, 75, 83
   Assyrian mythology 77
   Aztec mythology 52–3, *53*
mountains 21, 27
   creation 58
   magic 58, *109*
   moving 58
Mummu 18–19
Muninn 100
Murirangawhenua 24
music 96–9, 153, 181
muskrats 32–3, 35
Muspell 21–2, 45
Mycenae 144
myths 7–8
   and religion 8–9

Naglfar 45
Nana 10–11, 115
Nanna 41, 42
Napaeae 130
Narcissus 130–1, *130*, *131*
Native American mythology 15, 56
   Coyote and the Theft of Fire 66–7
   creation myths 32–5, *32*, *33*
   Lightning and the Sack of Storms 88–9
   Little Star and the Chief's Daughter 180–1

   Mondamin and the Indian Corn 124–7, *126*
   Sky Spirit and Fine Weather Woman 60–1
Nattier, Jean-Marc *140*
Nauru 30–1
Naxos *12*, 156, 157
Nemean Lion *144*, 145, *148*
Neolithic cultures 13
Nephthys 29, 119
Nereus 150
New Zealand 24–5, *24*, *25*, 58
Nidavellir 23
Nidhogg 100
Niflheim 20–1, 23, 39, 40, 42, 45, 100
Night 22, 27, 52–3, 65
   Evening Star 55
Nihongi 26
Nilakantha 37
Nile river 116–19
Ninevah 76
Ningizzida 83
Ninsun 78
Nissyen 170, 174
Noah 35
Norns, the 23, 100
Norse mythology 3, 6, 14, 31, 59, 179
   creation myth 20–3, *20*, *22*, *23*, 38–45
   Death of Balder the Beautiful 38–43, *41*, *42*
   death of Odin 100–1
   Golden Apples of Idun 72–5, *73*
   Moon-dogs 151
   Odin and the Mead of All-Knowing 92–5
   Ragnarok 44–5
North 22, 54, 64, 89
Notus 64
Nuadu Airgetlám 137
Nun 28
Nut 28–9, *29*
nuts 72, 75
nymphs 130–1

O no Yasumaro 26
oceans *see* seas and oceans
Odahmin 125
Odin 9, *20*, 21–3, *23*, 38–42, *39*, *44*, 73–5, 92, 94, 96

death 100–1, 125
  Odin and the Mead of
    All-Knowing 92–5
Odrorir 93–5, *93*
Odyssey, The 64–5, *64*
Oedipus 137
Ojibwe 124–7
Okahahwis 125
Old Spider 30–1
Olla 59
ollamh 95
Olympus, Mount 68
Omeme 125
oracles 138, 143, 144, 163
Oreads 130–1
Original Sin 10
Orpheus 92, 96–9, *96, 97,
  98, 99*
Osiris 9, 12, 29, *112,* 116–
  19, *116, 117, 118,* 127
otters 32–3
owls 179
Oya 59

paganism 9, 10–12
Pah 89
pantheistic mythologies 9
Parijata, Tree of Paradise
  35
Parmigianino *162*
Pârvati 14, 134–5
Pasiphaë 153, 154–5
patriarchal mythology 11–
  12, 13, 19, 25, 53
Pawnee 88–9
peacock 153
Pegasus 141
Peneius river 147
pentacle 75
Persephone (Proserpine)
  14, 92, 98–9, 120–3, *120,
  122, 123,* 166–7
Perseus 13, 137, 138–41,
  140, 142
Persian mythology 13, 53
personification 14
Phaedra 157
Phorcys *139*
Phrygian mythology 115
Picot, François *163*
Pillars of Hercules 144
Pluto *92*
poetic powers 95
  Orpheus 92, 96–9, *96,
    97, 98, 99*
Pole Star 89
Pollaiolo, Antonio *145*

Polydectes 138–9, *140,* 141
Polynesian mythology 59
  creation myths 24–5, *24,
    25,* 30–1, *30*
  see also Maori
    mythology
pomegranates 11, 115, 122
Poseidon 148, 153, 154–5,
  157
Poussin, Nicholas *131*
pregnancy see birth;
  conception, miraculous
Preserver 14
Prometheus 68–9, *68, 69,*
  150
Prosperpine see
  Persephone
Pryderi 174
Psyche 162–7, *163, 164,
  166, 167*
Puerto Rican mythology
  59
Puketapu 58
Pyrrha 35
pyxis 167

quests 133
  see also trials
Quetzalcoatl 9, *11,* 48, 54–
  5, *54*
Quetzalpetlatl 55

Ra 29, 83
race memory 12–14
Rackham, Arthur *73*
Ragnar Lodbrog 179
Ragnarok 44–5
rain 63
  Indra, Vishnu and the
    Demon of Drought
    158–9
rainbows
  Assyrian mythology 79
  Bifröst 23, 39, 45, 59, 74,
    74, 75
  bridge of heaven 59, *74*
  Mist and Rainbow 56–9
  Norse mythology 23
  Rainbow Serpent 59
Ratatosk 100
ravens 34–5, *35,* 92, *94,*
  100, 170, 175, 181
rebirth see resurrection
  and rebirth
reflections 131, *131,* 141
  see also mirrors
reincarnation 89

religion
  animism 14–15
  montheism and
    pantheism 9
  and mythology 8–9
resurrection and rebirth
  10, 12, 37
  Attis 115
  baptism 125
  butterfly as symbol of
    167
  corn gods 127
  Demeter and
    Persephone 12–3, *120,
    121, 122, 123*
  initiation rites 125
  Isis and Osiris 116–19,
    116, 117, 118, 119
  Maui and the Waters of
    Life 86–7, *86*
  Mithra and Christmas
    Day 53
  Odin 100–1
  vegetation deities
    112–15
  see also death;
    immortality, quest for
Rhadamanthys 154
riddles 179
Ringhorn 41
rivers 20-1, 98
rocks and stones 21, 58
Roman de la Rose 130
Roman mythology 162–7
Rubens, Peter Paul 152
Rudolf, Johann Baptist 65
runes 101, *101*

sacrifice 100–1, 125, 129,
  141
  Theseus and the
    Minotaur 152, 154–7
Sahwa 125
Sakaki tree 49
Samhain *104*
Samildánach 137
Sarpedon 154
satyrs 122
Savai'i 58
saviour gods 116, 127
Saxon mythology 85
Schoolcraft, Henry Rowe
  124
Schwind, Moritz von *166*
Scottish mythology 166
Sea of Oblivion 81–2
seas and oceans 13, 30

Bull from the Sea 152–4
Churning of the Ocean
  of Milk 36–7, *37*
creation 21, 31
creator-destroyer
  goddess 87
end of the world 45
goddesses born from *10,
  11*
sea gifts 37
sea monsters 25
seasons 48–9, 51, 111
  How Winter Came into
    the World 120–3
  Ishtar and Tammuz
    112–15, *112, 113, 114,
    115*
  Isis and Osiris 116–19,
    116, 117, 118, 119
Selene 129
Sellaio, Jacopo del *164*
Semitic peoples 12–13, 18
Seriphos 138, 141
serpents 7, 18, 22, 45, 75,
  82–3, 97
  and Hercules *142, 143*
  Hydra of Lerna 145–6,
    145, 148
  Quetzalcoatl 54, *54*
  Rainbow Serpent 59
  Serpent of Eternity *36*
  Serpent of Regeneration
    12, 83
  serpent–hair 14, *138,
    139, 139, 141*
  serpent–skirt 52, *53*
  Vâsuki, King of the
    Serpents 36–7, *37*
Set 29, 116–17, 119, *119*
seven veils 79, 114, *114*
Shades 97, *98*
Shahbomin 125
shaktis 134
Shakura 89
shamans 15, 72, 125
Shamash 78–9, 114
Shannon river *172*
shells 7, 30–1, *30,* 60
Shintoism 26–7
ships 41, 45
Shiva 14, 37, 134–5
Shu 28
siblings 26–7, 52–3
  Isis and Osiris 116–19,
    116, 117, 118, 119
  see also brothers; sisters
Siduri Sabitu 81

Signol, Emile *167*
Sîn 114
Sirens *15, 64, 97*
Sirius 119
sisters 13–14, *14*, 23, 57–9, 113–15, *139*
    weird 31
    see also siblings
Sisyphus 98
Siva *18*
skalds 95
Skoll 22, 44
skulls, necklace of *53*
sky
    creation 19, 21, 28–9, *29*
    gender 28
    gods 18–19, 53, 68
    Sky Spirit and Fine Weather Woman 60–1
sleep 82, 83
Sleeping Beauty 109
Sleipnir 39, *39*
Smith, Colonel H. *67*
snakes *see* serpents
snow 61
Snow White 75
Soatsaki 180–1
soil 21
Sol Invictus 13, 53
solstices 38, 53
    eight-yearly cycle 153, 156
Soma 37
Son 93–5
son-lovers 137, 169
sons 129, 137
sorcerors 54
South 22, 54, 64, 89
Spider Man 180–1
spiders 7, 30–1, 106–7
spinning 30, 31, 106–7
    Arachne 106–7, *107*
    Cowherd and the Heavenly Spinner 62–3, *63*
    Thread of Destiny 30, 31, 106
    see also weaving
springs 20, 23, 100
    Fountain of Forgetfulness 166
    Fountain of Parthenius 168
    Fountain of Youth 37
    Spring of Enlightenment 100
Stables of Augeias 147

stars
    Aztec mythology 52–3
    Cowherd and the Heavenly Spinner 62–3, *63*
    creation 19, 21–2, *28*
    Egyptian mythology *28*
    Evening Star 54–5
    Native American mythology 89
    Ragnarok 45
    Star of Knowledge 75
Stella Maris (Star of the Sea) 11
Sthenelus 143
Stheno 139, 141
storms 18, 27, 34, 48, 158–9
    Fine Weather Woman 61
    Lightning and the Sack of Storms 88–9
Stymphalus, Birds of 146
Styx 98, 166–7
Sun
    Assyrian mythology 81
    Aztec mythology 52–3
    creation 22, 31, 37, 84
    Death of Balder the Beautiful 38–43, *41, 42*
    eight-yearly cycle 153, 156
    goddess 27, 48–9, *48, 49*
    gods 83, 137
    in Hiding 48–9, *48, 49*
    and Little Star 180–1
    Maui and the Waters of Life 86–7
    Native American mythology 89
    Ragnarok 45
    Sol Invictus
    solar bull 153, 156, 169
    solar heroes 53
    Sun Dance *180*, 181
Surabhi 37
Surt 45
Susano-Wo 27, 48–9
Svartalfheim 23
sword bridge 59
Symplegades 58
Syrian mythology 115

Tacitus 169
Taka-Mi-Musubi-No-Kami 26
Taliesin 11, 102–5, 174
Tama-No-Ya 49

tamarisk 12, 117–18
Tammuz 12, 79, 112–15
Tantalus 98
Tara 136–7, *136*
Tarot *100*, 151
tauropárthenos 153
Tawhaki 59
Te Ika-a-Maui 25
Tefnut 28
Tenochtitlan 52
Tezcatlipoca 9, 52, 54–5, 55
Thanatos 149
theft
    of fire 66–9
    Lightning and the Sack of Storms 88–9
    serpents 83, *83*
Themis 35
Theseus 12, *134*, 152, 153, *154*, 155–7, *155*
Thespius, King 143
Thjazi 74–5
Thomas the Rhymer 75
Thor 6, 13, 41, *42*, 101
Thoth 29, 119
Thread of Destiny 30, 31, 106
Thrymheim 74–5
thunder 6, 18–19, 27, 45, 53, 68, 89
Tiamat 12, 18–19, 25
Tintoretto *107, 157*
Tirawa 88–9
Titans 68
Titian 168
Toltec mythology *48*, 54–5, *54*
Toneri, Prince 26
Tower of London 174, *175, 175*
Trampler 19
trees 12, 22–3, 27, 35, 49, 117–18
    axis mundi (world tree) 23, *23*, 45
    sacrificial 100–1
    Tree of Happiness 23
    Tree of Life 12, 83
    Tree of Paradise 35
    Tree of Truth 83
trials 7, 133
    Cinderella 166
    Durgâ and the Demon 134–5, *134, 135*
    initiation rites 7, 125, 151

Perseus and the Gorgon 13, 137, 138–41, *138, 139, 140, 141*
Psyche 165–7
riddles 179
sword or hair bridge 59
Twelve Labours of Hercules *13*, 144–51, *144, 145, 147*
trickster 7, 24–5, 66, 85, 86–7
Trinity 12, *18*, 31, 62
Triple Goddesses 14, *14*, 48, 75
Triple Gods 21
Triptolemus 121, *122*
Tsuki-Yomi 27, *27*
Tuatha Dé Danann 136–7
turtles 33, *33*, 37
Tvashtri 158–9
Twelfth Night 122
twins 142

Uenuku 57–9
Ulysses 15, 64–5, *64*
Uma 134
underworld 97–9, 120–3, 166–7
Unkulunkulu 84–5
Up-Uat 89
Uranus 143
Urshanabi 81–2
Uruk 76
Uta-Napishtim 35, 81–2

Vajra 159
Valhalla 45
Vanaheim 23
Vanir, the 23, 92–3
Vâsuki, King of the Serpents 36–7, *37*
Ve 21–2
vegetation deities 110–31
Venus *see* Aphrodite
Vigrid 45
Vikings *see* Norse mythology
Vili 21–2
violets 115
Virgil the Gaul 102
virgin birth 10–12, 52–3, 115, 177
virgin goddess 169
Virgin Mary 10–12
Vishnu 7, 14, *18, 36*, 37, 158–9
Vritra 159

warrior gods 18, 53, 54
water 67
Watts, Frederick *98*
weather
  drought, demon of
    158–9
  Sky Spirit and Fine
    Weather Woman 60–1
  see also lightning; rain;
    storms; thunder; wind
weaving 49, 106–7
  Secret of Weaving 108–9
  shuttle, prick by 49
  see also spinning
weird sisters 31
Well of Urd (Well of Fate)
  23, 100
Welsh mythology 102–5,
  170–9
  see also Celtic
  mythology

West 22, *54*, 64, 89
West Wind *see* Zephyrus
whales 37, 51
Wheel of Fortune 31
wind 19, 27, 34, 54, 89
  Ulysses and the Bag of
    Winds 64–5, *64*, *65*
wine 127, 128–9
winter 51, 120–3, 124–7
  Sun in Hiding 48–9, *48*,
    49
  see also seasons
wives, fairy 57–9, 108–9
Wolf Trail 181
wolves 22, 34, 44–5, *44*, 89,
  89
wonder tales 7, 8
Wunzh 124–7

Xipe Totec 54
Xochiquetzal 35

Yahweh *see* Jehovah
Yansa 59
year, lunar division 104
Yggdrasil 23, *23*, 45, 100
yin and yang 59
Ymir *20*, 21
Ynawg 174
Yomi 27
Yoruban mythology 59

Zephyrus (West Wind) 64,
  163, 164
Zeus 12, 13
  and Alcmene 142
  bull myths 153
  Cupid and Psyche 167
  and Danaë 138
  Demeter myth 121–2
  Dionysus and the Vine
    128
  Echo myth 130

and Europa *152*, 153,
  153, 154
and Io 107, 152–4
and Prometheus 68–9
Zick, Alexander *68*
Ziusudra 35
zodiac 156
Zulu mythology
  Message of
    Unkulunkulu 84–5
Zuni Indian mythology
  the elements 67

ACKNOWLEDGEMENTS

Front cover and spine, **AKG** Rennes, Musée des Beaux-Arts, Erich Lessing, Back cover & arlin, **Reed Consumer Books Ltd,** Endpapers, **AKG.**

AKG, London 6, 14, 68, 92, 97, 99, 118, 128, 132-133, 143, 146, 166, /Athens, National Archaeological Museum 122, /Banca Toscana, Florence, Italy 15,/Berlin, Pergamon-Museum 139, /Bibliotheque Nationale, Paris 130, /Dayr-az-Zaqr, Syria 113 Top,/Dept. des Antiquités Grecques et Romaines, Paris, Musée du Louvre 13, /Dresden, Gemaeldegalerie, Alte Meister 120,/Erich Lessing, Eleusis Archeological Museum 2–3,/Erich Lessing, Munich, Glyptothek 4–5, /Kiev, Museum of Western & Eastern Art 90–91,/Madrid, Museo del Prado 152,/Musée du Louvre, Paris 1, 69, 131, 144, 168,/National Gallery, London 169, /Venice, Palace of the Doge 156,/Vienna, Akademie der Bildenden Kuenste 129,/Vienna, Kunsthistorisches Museum 110–111, 119, 150, 153, 162,/Vienna, Museum der Stadt Wien 106,/Wuerzburg, Staatsgalerie 65. **Axel Poignant** 86.**Bridgeman Art Library** 87,/A. M. Gillion Crowet, Brussels/Giraudon 96,/Biblioteca Nazionale Centrale, Florence

46–47,/Bibliotheque Nationale, Paris 123,/British Museum, London 19, 27 Top,/Chapel of the Planets, Tempio Malatestiano, Rimini 82,/Christie's, London 160,/Fitzwilliam Museum, University of Cambridge 148, 164,/Forbes Magazine Collection, New York 98,/Freud Museum, London 7,/Galleria Degli Uffizi, Florence 107, 138, 145,/Louvre, Paris 18, 29, 70–71, 112, 163,/Louvre, Paris, Lauros-Giraudon 76,/Manchester City Art Galleries 41,/Musée de Petit Palais, Avignon 157,/Musée des Beaux-Arts, Tours 140,/Museo Archeologico Nazionale, Naples 155,/Museo du Bardo, Tunis 64,/National Library of Australia, Canberra 50,/National Museum of Iceland, Reykjavik 42 left,/National Museum of India, New Delhi 16–17, 158,/Natural History Museum, London 33, 67,/Oxford University Museum of Natural History, England 83,/Phillips, The International Fine Art Auctioneers 58,/Private Collection 25, 32, 85, 100, 167, 180,/Royal Geographical Society 56, 108/Royal Library, Copenhagen 40, 45,/Stapleton Collection 84,/The De Morgan Foundation, London 121,/Victoria & Albert Museum 60, 88. **Corbis UK Ltd** 20, 30, 34, 37, 48, 66. **Mary**

Evans Picture Library 23, 35, 43, 72, 73, 74, 79, 80, 94, 114, 124, 126, 159. **Werner Forman Archive** 22, 27 Bottom, 44 Top,/Arhus Kunstmuseum, Denmark 38,/British Museum, London 9, 28, 54, 116,/Courtesy L'Ibis, New York 117,/Denpasar Museum, Bali 10,/Liverpool Museum 55,/National Gallery, Prague 36,/National Museum of Anthropology, Mexico City 11, 52,/National Museum, Athens 8,/Statens Histoiska Museum, Stockholm 39, 42 Right. **Getty Images** 105, 175. **Godsfield Press**/taken from 'The Celtic Book of Days' by Caitlin Matthews, thanks to the Bridgewater Book Company 104. **Reed Consumer Books Ltd.** 12, 24, 26, 44 Bottom, 49, 53, 77, 78, 93, 100–101, 102, 109, 113, 115, 134, 135, 141, 142, 154. **National Library of Wales,** Department of Pictures and Maps/Illustration by Stuart Littlejohn from 'The Song of Taliesin' by John Matthews 103, /Illustration courtesy of Welsh Books Council and Margaret Jones from 'Tales of the Mabinogion' by Gwyn Thomas & Kevin Crossley-Holland 170, 171, 172–173, 174, 176, 177, 178. **Don Sutton International Photo Library** 136. **Victoria & Albert Museum** 62, 63.